Macmillan/McGraw-Hill Science

EARTH'S ECOSYSTEMS

AUTHORS

Mary Atwater
The University of Georgia

Prentice Baptiste
University of Houston

Lucy Daniel
Rutherford County Schools

Jay Hackett
University of Northern Colorado

Richard Moyer
University of Michigan, Dearborn

Carol Takemoto
Los Angeles Unified School District

Nancy Wilson
Sacramento Unified School District

Earth from space

D1307752

Macmillan/McGraw-Hill
School Publishing Company
New York   Columbus

MACMILLAN / McGRAW-HILL

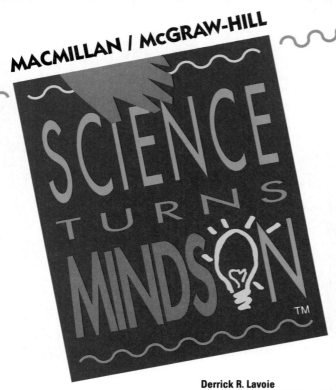

SCIENCE TURNS MINDS ON™

Environmental Education:
Cheryl Charles, Ph.D.
Executive Director
Project Wild
Boulder, CO

Gifted:
Dr. James A. Curry
Associate Professor, Graduate Faculty
College of Education, University of Southern Maine
Gorham, ME

Global Education:
M. Eugene Gilliom
Professor of Social Studies and Global Education
The Ohio State University
Columbus, OH

Life Science:
Wyatt W. Anderson
Professor of Genetics
University of Georgia
Athens, GA

Orin G. Gelderloos
Professor of Biology and Professor of Environmental Studies
University of Michigan—Dearborn
Dearborn, MI

Donald C. Lisowy
Education Specialist
New York, NY

Dr. E.K. Merrill
Assistant Professor
University of Wisconsin Center—Rock County
Madison, WI

Literature:
Dr. Donna E. Norton
Texas A&M University
College Station, TX

CONSULTANTS

Assessment:
Mary Hamm
Associate Professor
Department of Elementary Education
San Francisco State University
San Francisco, CA

Cognitive Development:
Pat Guild, Ed.D.
Director, Graduate Programs in Education and
Learning Styles Consultant
Antioch University
Seattle, WA

Kathi Hand, M.A.Ed.
Middle School Teacher and Learning Styles Consultant
Assumption School
Seattle, WA

Derrick R. Lavoie
Assistant Professor of Science Education
Montana State University
Bozeman, MT

Earth Science:
David G. Futch
Associate Professor of Biology
San Diego State University
San Diego, CA

Dr. Shadia Rifai Habbal
Harvard-Smithsonian Center for Astrophysics
Cambridge, MA

Tom Murphree, Ph.D.
Global Systems Studies
Monterey, CA

Suzanne O'Connell
Assistant Professor
Wesleyan University
Middletown, CT

Sidney E. White
Professor of Geology
The Ohio State University
Columbus, OH

Macmillan/McGraw-Hill School Division
10 Union Square East
New York, New York 10003
Printed in the United States of America

ISBN 0-02-276136-5 / 7

3 4 5 6 7 8 9 RRW 99 98 97 96

Mathematics:
Dr. Richard Lodholz
Parkway School District
St. Louis, MO

Middle School Specialist:
Daniel Rodriguez
Principal
Pomona, CA

Misconceptions:
Dr. Charles W. Anderson
Michigan State University
East Lansing, MI

Dr. Edward L. Smith
Michigan State University
East Lansing, MI

Multicultural:
Bernard L. Charles
Senior Vice President
Quality Education for Minorities Network
Washington, DC

Paul B. Janeczko
Poet
Hebron, MA

James R. Murphy
Math Teacher
La Guardia High School
New York, NY

Clifford E. Trafzer
Professor and Chair, Ethnic Studies
University of California, Riverside
Riverside, CA

Physical Science:
Gretchen M. Gillis
Geologist
Maxus Exploration Company
Dallas, TX

Henry C. McBay
Professor of Chemistry
Morehouse College and Clark Atlanta University
Atlanta, GA

Wendell H. Potter
Associate Professor of Physics
Department of Physics
University of California, Davis
Davis, CA

Claudia K. Viehland
Educational Consultant, Chemist
Sigma Chemical Company
St. Louis, MO

Reading:
Charles Temple, Ph.D.
Associate Professor of Education
Hobart and William Smith Colleges
Geneva, NY

Safety:
Janice Sutkus
Program Manager: Education
National Safety Council
Chicago, IL

Science Technology and Society (STS):
William C. Kyle, Jr.
Director, School Mathematics and Science Center
Purdue University
West Lafayette, IN

Social Studies:
Jean Craven
District Coordinator of Curriculum Development
Albuquerque Public Schools
Albuquerque, NM

Students Acquiring English:
Mario Ruiz
Pomona, CA

STUDENT ACTIVITY TESTERS

Alveria Henderson
Kate McGlumphy
Katherine Petzinger
John Wirtz
Sarah Wittenbrink

Andrew Duffy
Chris Higgins
Sean Pruitt
Joanna Huber
John Petzinger

FIELD TEST TEACHERS

Kathy Bowles
Landmark Middle School
Jacksonville, FL

Myra Dietz
#46 School
Rochester, NY

John Gridley
H.L. Harshman Junior High School #101
Indianapolis, IN

Annette Porter
Schenk Middle School
Madison, WI

Connie Boone
Fletcher Middle School
Jacksonville, FL

Theresa Smith
Bates Middle School
Annapolis, MD

Debbie Stamler
Sennett Middle School
Madison, WI

Margaret Tierney
Sennett Middle School
Madison, WI

Mel Pfeiffer
I.P.S. #94
Indianapolis, IN

CONTRIBUTING WRITER

Elizabeth Alexander

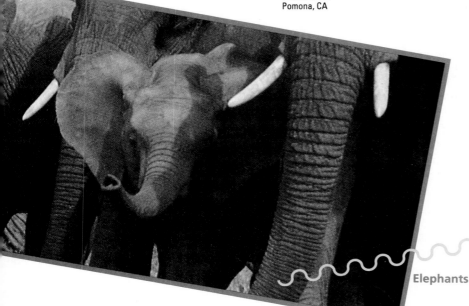

Elephants

3

Earth's Ecosystems

Lessons   Themes

Activities!

EXPLORE

TRY THIS

Features

 Links

Literature Link

Social Studies Link

Math Link

Language Arts Link

CAREERS

SCIENCE TECHNOLOGY and Society

Departments

Northern Spotted Owl

Earth's Ecosystems

AS THE SPIDER'S WEB VIBRATES WITH EACH SPIDERY MOVEMENT AND
WIND CURRENT, SO OUR ECOSYSTEM VIBRATES WITH THE MOVEMENTS
OF ALL ORGANISMS. MOVEMENTS MAY AFFECT THE SPIDER WEB OR
THEY MAY AFFECT THE WEB'S SUPPORTING ELEMENTS. SO IT IS
WITH OUR ECOSYSTEM.

◆　◆　◆　◆　◆

The study of how living things, including you, interact with
each other and their environment is called ecology. In this unit you
will act as an ecologist, a scientist who studies these interactions.
You will explore an ecosystem's plants, animals, and other living
things, noting how they interact and form a system with the environment in which they live. You will explore a tropical rain forest
and the animals and plants within it. You will learn of organisms
that owe their survival to humans awakening to the limitations of
the environment. You will be challenged to help reduce destructive
human impact on the environment.

The study of how organisms interact with each other in an ecosystem is called *ecology*.

The trash you generate does not just disappear. It is either burned, goes to a landfill, or is dumped into the ocean.

Used clothing, old television sets, broken sports equipment, and fast-food wrappers don't just disappear when you're done using them. Some trash goes to landfills, and some is burned or recycled. Trash continues to interact with the environment even when in a landfill—it takes up space and may harm the environment.

Minds On! You can get a rough idea of the trash you are leaving on Earth by listing everything you throw away for one week in your *Activity Log* on page 1. Make sure you include everything—gum wrappers, packaging from items you buy or meals you eat, magazines, and even the food you throw away at mealtimes. At the end of the week, review your list. Find out where these items went when you threw them away. Were any of the things you threw away hazardous materials?

Contact your state Environmental Protection Agency for information on hazardous wastes. You may be surprised to find out that some items you thought were harmless are actually harmful to the environment. Are there some ways you could decrease the amount of trash you throw away?●

What you do affects your environment—near and far. The study of these environments and their living organisms has fascinated scientists. Some scientists specialize in counting the

numbers of certain animals. Some study the relationships of plants and animals and environment. Some specialize in one environment that fascinates them. The tropical rain forest has long been studied by ecologists and environmentalists. In the Try This Activity on this page, you will make an enclosed environment similar in many ways to one type of environment you will study in this unit.

Activity!

Make an Ecosystem!

How do living things besides humans interact with each other and their environment? You can observe this when you make an enclosed ecosystem, or area, where living organisms and their physical surroundings interact.

What You Need

gravel, soil, rocks, sticks
ferns, moss, small plants, water plants
grass seeds, other seeds
insects, earthworms
snails, salamanders, small toads or frogs

plastic bowl	**lettuce, ground beef**
terrarium	**screen cover**
pulverized charcoal	***Activity Log* page 2**

Place a 2-cm layer of gravel on the bottom of the terrarium, and cover the gravel first with a layer of charcoal and then with a 4-cm layer of soil. Arrange the rocks to make a small cave. Moisten the soil, and set the plants in it. Plant some seeds in the soil, too.

Bury the plastic bowl so it becomes a small pond in the terrarium. Fill the pond with water; then, add algae or a water plant such as *Elodea*. Place a few rocks in the pond.

Add earthworms and insects such as ants or crickets to your terrarium. If you can collect snails, salamanders, small frogs or toads, add those to your ecosystem as well. Record in your ***Activity Log*** what kind and how many organisms you add to the terrarium.

Place a screen cover over the top, and put the terrarium in a well-lighted place. Don't allow the pond to dry out—if the water level gets too low, add more water. You may also have to water the soil occasionally. If you add snails, feed them a little lettuce every day. If you add toads, frogs, or salamanders, feed them ground beef (the amount that would cover a dime per organism) every day. As you go through this unit, you will revisit your ecosystem to observe and relate the relationships and changes you are studying. Record all your observations in your ***Activity Log.***

Science in Literature

STEP INTO THE WORLD OF ECOLOGISTS, BIOLOGISTS, AND OTHER SCIENTISTS
THROUGH THE DOORWAY OF BOOKS—INTO THE SWAMP, INTO THE TINY ECOSYSTEMS
UNDER THE FLOORBOARDS OF YOUR HOME. DISCOVER THE MYSTERY OF
THE RAIN FORESTS AND THE PREDICAMENT OF THE WHALE.
THROUGH THE BOOKS DESCRIBED BELOW AND OTHERS YOUR TEACHER MAY SUGGEST,
YOU CAN ENLARGE YOUR UNDERSTANDING OF ECOSYSTEMS, ENJOY THE ABUNDANCE OF
THE TROPICAL RAIN FORESTS, AND FIND WAYS YOU CAN PROTECT
THE ENVIRONMENT AND ITS ORGANISMS.

Seeds of Change

**by Sarah Sargent.
New York: Bradbury Press, 1989.**

What started as a depressing prospect—spending a summer in a Georgia swamp away from fun and friends—turned into the adventure of Rachel's life. Rachel's father, an energetic entrepreneur, buys the swamp to develop it into a theme park. The only thing that Rachel has to look forward to is a chance to show her father she can be an entrepreneur, too.

Determined to make the best of it, Rachel investigates the swamp—solely for the purpose of gathering theme park ideas. She finds much more than she expected. The swamp isn't what it seems—frightening animals, shifting soil, inexplicable sounds, a flower that is not quite a flower, and at the center of the swamp, the strangest surprise of all.

As Rachel experiences the swamp, she begins to understand that it is a complex world of its own, with a special beauty, home to unique creatures. Then Rachel has to ask herself what place development has in this world. Can humans and swamps coexist?

This book will take you on a vivid trip through a mysterious Georgia swamp and provoke questions about the relationship of humans to Earth. Read it along with or right after Lesson 2 on biomes.

Small Worlds

by Howard E. Smith, Jr.
New York: Charles Scribner
and Sons, 1987.

Do you imagine you have to visit a park, the mountains, or a desert to observe interactions among organisms? You will be surprised to discover the life that exists in unlikely places. Your home may have interdependent organisms living in it. A patch of grass on the side of a road, a sheer rock cliff, and a city lot are all ecosystems.

Each chapter describes a different ecosystem in terms of ecological concepts. How do the living and nonliving factors in the environments affect the organisms living there? How do the populations in the communities interact? What is the food chain for each ecosystem? Use the examples in the book to further illustrate the concepts and to guide you through one of these ecosystems near you.

Other Good Books To Read

Earthworms, Dirt, and Rotten Leaves by Molly McLaughlin. New York: Atheneum, 1986.

The lowly earthworm does more than act as fish bait. By doing the activities in this book, you not only learn about the earthworm, but also understand its niche in our ecosystem.

Jungle Rescue: Saving the New World Tropical Rain Forests by Christina G. Miller and Louise A. Berry. New York: Atheneum, 1991.

Humans are endangering the fragile rain forests, but there is something you can do to save them. This book explains the relationship between plants, insects, animals, and humans and gives specific activities to increase your understanding of the fragility of this dramatically beautiful environment.

Can the Whales Be Saved? by Dr. Philip Whitfield. New York: Viking Kestrel, 1989.

Do zoos and wildlife parks help save endangered animals? What is an oasis? Is the jungle noisy? From the usual questions to the unusual, this book tries to answer intriguing questions about nature. Color photographs and drawings illustrate when words can't do the job. This book can be picked up and read from cover to cover or article by article. Whichever way you read it, you will learn interesting facts about nature.

What Is an Ecosystem?

LIVING THINGS LIVE SIDE BY SIDE AND INTERACT WITH EACH OTHER AND WITH NONLIVING THINGS. IN THIS LESSON YOU WILL STUDY FACTORS IN ENVIRONMENTS THAT ENABLE THIS EXISTENCE.

◆　◆　◆　◆　◆

You are on a deserted tropical island—white beaches and coconut palms, hot afternoon sun, and balmy breezes. There are scampering lizards and clear, rushing streams. It sounds like a paradise—much different from where most of us live. Life would be easy—at least in your daydreams. After a while, if you were stranded here, you might begin to miss things you know. You would find plants and animals different from those at home. You would have to adjust and learn about living in a new environment.

Minds On! It's Monday morning and you and your family find yourselves stranded on an island without food or shelter. You're hungry. How are you going to eat? How will you keep dry if it rains? List things your family would need to survive on the island. Include in your list how you would use the island's resources to get the necessities for survival.●

You probably decided that survival was possible on the tropical island. You anticipated what you could eat and how you would find shelter. Being able to come up with survival strategies means that you already knew something about what living things need from an ecosystem to survive and how individuals and ecosystems interact. In this lesson you will learn more about interactions in an ecosystem. In the Explore Activity that follows, you will observe an organism in its specialized ecosystem.

If you were stranded on an island, the ecosystem you would interact with would be limited.

Activity!

What Factors Affect Where Brine Shrimp Live?

You thought about what plants and animals might live on the island pictured on pages 12 and 13. What you already know about environments gave you some clues about the types of things you might find on the island. In this Activity, you'll investigate the way an environment can affect something that might live in the waters around your island.

What You Need

1 large, wide-mouthed jar
brine
warm tap water
vial of brine shrimp eggs
masking tape
hand lens
1 package dry yeast
plastic spoon
brown paper bag
rubber band
flashlight
plastic shoe box
ice cube
self-sealing sandwich bag
Activity Log pages 4–5

What To Do

1 Pour the brine into the jar, filling it 3/4 full. Mark the level of the water with masking tape.

2 Take a look at the brine shrimp eggs with a hand lens and describe them in your *Activity Log*. Sprinkle 1/4 tsp. of brine shrimp eggs onto the surface of the water.

3 Set the jar in a warm, well-lighted place—but not in direct sunlight. Check the jar containing brine shrimp eggs every day, and add water to keep the water level at the tape mark. Use the hand lens to check for live brine shrimp. They will be tiny, almost invisible, but you can see them as white dots swimming around.

4 Once you see live shrimp, sprinkle just 5 or 6 grains of yeast on the water every day. If the water is milky, you are using too much yeast.

5 Take a few shrimp out on a spoon and observe them with a hand lens. Draw a picture of how the shrimp look in your *Activity Log*.

6 Make hypotheses as to how the brine shrimp will react to light, and hot and cold temperatures. Write your hypotheses in your *Activity Log.* Now test your hypotheses in steps 7–9.

7 Wrap the sides of the jar with brown paper and secure with a rubber band. Shine a flashlight onto the surface of the brine for 3 min. While holding the light in place, remove the paper. Record the location of most of the shrimp in your *Activity Log.*

8 Gently pour the brine and shrimp into a plastic shoe box. Seal an ice cube inside a sandwich bag. Put the bag in the brine at one end of the plastic shoe box. After 5 min, record where most of the shrimp are located in your *Activity Log.*

9 Remove the bag and dispose of the ice cube. Put some warm tap water in the bag and seal it. Place it where the ice cube was. After 5 min, record where the shrimp are now located.

What Happened?

1. How did the shrimp respond to light? Was your hypothesis correct?
2. What did the shrimp eat?
3. How did the brine shrimp respond to cold water? Warm water? Were your hypotheses correct?
4. What is the energy source for the environment in the jar?
5. Why was it important not to cover the jar containing the brine shrimp?

What Now?

1. What physical conditions in the jar are similar to the ocean? What conditions are different?
2. Where in the ocean do you think you would find brine shrimp?
3. What would happen if you placed some brine shrimp eggs in distilled water with no salt?
4. Make a list of the environmental factors brine shrimp need in order to live.

EXPLORE

What Makes Up an Ecosystem?

In the Minds On on page 12, you listed the things you and your family would need to survive in the island ecosystem. Your family depended upon the physical environment of the island to meet survival needs. In the Explore Activity, you observed how brine shrimp react to changes in their salt-water environment. Each environment (the island and the jar) and its animals (the family and the shrimp) is an ecosystem. An **ecosystem** is made up of a physical environment and all the living and nonliving things within this area.

Like all living things, you need water to survive. Water is important, but what it contains can greatly affect living things. You discovered that brine shrimp live in water with salt dissolved in it, and that they prefer warm water and light. Where might such an environment be found in the ocean?

Like the brine shrimp, your choice of environment is determined by light and heat. Would you choose to live in a cave on your island, or would there be better "housing" for you and your family? What might happen if you had no shelter from the tropical sun?

In the Minds On, you probably thought right away about what you would eat while stranded on the island. You probably couldn't survive on tree bark, but you could eat coconuts. You would find yourself eating what was available in the island environment. In the Explore Activity, brine shrimp behaved similarly. Your shrimp ate the yeast you provided, but in the ocean brine shrimp eat other one-celled organisms.

Water, light, temperature, and the availability of food or essential nutrients affected the life of the brine shrimp. These physical parts of the ecosystem determine what and how many organisms can live there.

Both the shrimp and your family are living organisms in an ecosystem. The living parts of an ecosystem, such as plants and animals, are called **biotic** (bī ot′ ik) **factors.** The nonliving parts, such as soil and light, are called **abiotic** (ā′ bī ot′ ik) **factors.** What factors were abiotic in the saltwater jar and on the island? The interactions between the biotic and abiotic parts in an environment allow it to function as an ongoing system.

Minds On! Imagine you are back on your island. You have lived there for one year. How have you changed the ecosystem in that time? In your *Activity Log* on page 6, make a list of possible effects you and your family could have on the island ecosystem.●

Biotic factors affect the ecosystem—the tree's branches create an environment for shade-loving plants.

Abiotic factors have affected the growth of this bristlecone pine.

Biotic and Abiotic Factors

Biotic and abiotic factors interact. All organisms have some impact on their environment—they eat, excrete wastes, take up space. Some organisms even change the physical environment—farmers often plant trees along a field to reduce erosion. Trees slow the wind, which in turn slows erosion. The shade under a tree prevents sunlight from reaching the ground, cooling the area in the shade. When the tree was young, the shade provided at the trunk was only a very small area, but as the tree grew, so did the shaded area. A large oak tree prevents most sunlight from reaching the ground beneath it. The shade lowers the temperature at ground level, encouraging the growth of shade-loving plants in an increasing area.

Revisit the ecosytem you made in the Try This Activity on page 9. Observe and record, in your *Activity Log* page 3, how the biotic and abiotic factors interact in the terrarium.

Light, water, and temperature are the determining factors in where land plants can live. Soil contains the nutrients plants need. Different kinds of soil support different kinds of plants. In the following Try This Activity, you'll note some of the physical properties of different kinds of soil.

Activity!

What's in Soil?

Dirt is dirt, right? Well, scientists would say, "Soil is soil." How might one soil sample differ from another? The composition can affect what kind of life the soil can support. Using several soil samples, you will note the differences in the components of soil.

What You Need

3 samples of soil, 3 0.5-L jars with lids, masking tape, water, metric ruler, *Activity Log* page 7

Collect three soil samples, one each from different places, such as a garden, an empty lot, the edge of a stream, or around your school. Make sure you have permission to dig. Try to include more than just the top layer of soil. Fill each of three 0.5-L jars half full of one sample each. Label the jars by location and record in your *Activity Log* where the samples were taken. Then, add water until the jars are full. Cover the jars with lids and shake until the large soil particles break apart. Place the jars where they will not be disturbed overnight.

The next day, without moving the jars, use a metric ruler to measure the depth of each different layer you can see. In your *Activity Log,* record the depths of each sediment layer for each soil sample.

How did the soil samples compare? Is there a relationship between the area where you obtained the samples and the composition of the soil? Write the answers in your *Activity Log*.

Farmers hope to limit erosion in their ecosystem by planting trees.

The kind of soil (determined by varying mineral contents, nutrients, and amounts of water) helps determine the organisms that live there. Roses and asparagus grow in different types of soil. Prairie dogs and earthworms live in different types of soil. Specialized grasses and groundcovers grow best in specific soil types.

Some herd animals such as cattle change the physical environment when they overgraze. Overgrazing results in the destruction of plant life, which in turn changes the soil. Without plants, soil will erode and the ecosystem will change.

Humans are responsible for changes in the ecosystem. What began as the richness present in a North American ecosystem almost ended with the extinction of one organism. The diminishing of this organism's populations then affected a group of humans who depended upon it for survival. The following story is one that ecologists hope will not be repeated.

Buffalo Hunting

Before settlers moved westward into the Great Plains, enormous herds of American buffalo or bison roamed from Canada down through the United States. Native Americans who lived in this region hunted buffalo for food and used the hides for clothing and   shelter. The Native American populations weren't large. They didn't hunt more buffalo than they needed or waste any part of the animal. Native Americans were able to continue this life-style for as long as the buffalo population continued to flourish.

Many settlers valued buffalo hides as decorative items. Hunters killed buffalo for sport or for their hides, killing them in large numbers, skinning them, and leaving the carcasses on the plains. When they saw the huge herds that seemed to stretch forever, they hunted as though the supply of buffalo were unending. In time, buffalo populations became depleted until there were only small herds left. The food source of Plains tribes was seriously threatened, and people wondered if buffalo would become extinct. Fortunately, conservationists, people who try to save natural resources, worked to save the remaining herds in a protected environment. Today, while not as large as the herds of the 1800s, a healthy buffalo population lives in areas of the Great Plains.

Consider the differences between the settlers' and the Native Americans' use of the buffalo. In your *Activity Log* on page 8, compare the two and their effects. What were the consequences to the ecosystem? How were the lives of the buffalo and the Native Americans interdependent in their ecosystem?

Before mass hunting of buffalo, huge herds roamed the Great Plains.

Interactions That Cycle Materials

During the 1800s, buffalo were hunted as if the supply were endless. However, they were then, and are now, a limited resource. There are many other resources in today's world that people treat as though they are in unending supply—oil, natural gas, coal, and land. People have begun to recycle plastic, glass, aluminum, and paper with a renewed awareness that most resources are available in a limited supply. It's interesting to note that the idea of recycling or cycling resources is at work in Earth's ecosystems.

All parts of an ecosystem, living and nonliving, work together to continuously cycle water and other substances vital to life. Air, water, soil, and living organisms constantly exchange waste, carbon, and nitrogen. This cycling provides organisms with an ongoing supply of materials they need for survival, growth, and reproduction in an ecosystem.

The water cycle is of great interest to scientists, especially those working with developing clean water sources in areas of limited water supply.

The Water Cycle

Water is the most abundant resource on Earth, and one of the most important. All organisms depend on water for life. Water is constantly cycled between biotic and abiotic parts of an ecosystem. The cycle begins when water falls to the surface of Earth in the form of fog, dew, rain, hail, or snow. Once water falls to the ground, it follows several routes. Some of the moisture that falls seeps into the soil, and some collects in bodies of water like rivers, lakes, or oceans. Plants take in water from soil through their roots and eventually return water to the atmosphere by transpiration, the elimination of water vapor through the pores in their leaves. Heat from sunlight causes water held in soil or in bodies of water to evaporate. The water vapor then cools and falls to Earth, beginning the cycle again.

respiration

O_2

O_2

photosynthesis

CO_2

Recycling

The Carbon Cycle

J ust as water cycles through the ecosystem, so do the gases carbon dioxide and oxygen. These gases are needed by every living thing. Study the diagram below to follow the carbon cycle.

The carbon cycle involves two basic life processes, photosynthesis and respiration. Green plants absorb carbon dioxide from the air. During photosynthesis, plants make simple sugar using carbon dioxide and water. In the process, plants release oxygen into the air. Oxygen in the air is used by plants and animals in respiration. Oxygen combines with food and releases energy. Carbon dioxide is also released into the air to begin the cycle again. You are part of the carbon cycle when you breathe in oxygen, and then exhale carbon-dioxide into the atmosphere.

All organisms contain carbon. Waste products and the dead bodies of plants, animals, or simple organisms are broken down by bacteria called decomposers. The carbon in waste and decomposing bodies is released as carbon dioxide and rejoins the carbon cycle.

Coal, natural gas, and oil are carbon-containing materials made from the remains of organisms that died millions of years ago. When humans burn these substances as fuel, carbon dioxide is released into the atmosphere. The burnings of these fuels and the cutting down of forests is threatening the balance of the carbon cycle.

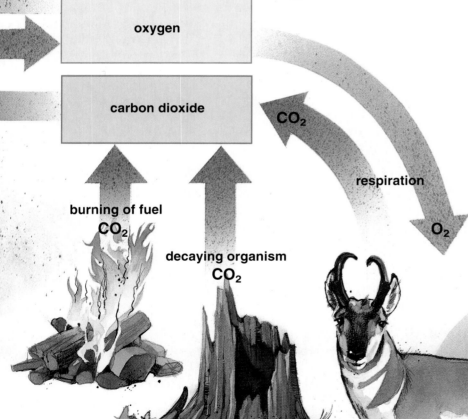

oxygen

carbon dioxide

CO_2

respiration

O_2

burning of fuel
CO_2

decaying organism
CO_2

The Nitrogen Cycle

Nitrogen is also essential for life—hereditary material and proteins, which all organisms contain, are made with nitrogen. Nitrogen is found as a gas in the atmosphere in large quantities, but most organisms can't use it in this form. Nitrogen is so important to plant growth that farmers and gardeners use nitrogen-containing fertilizers.

Some nitrogen gas is converted to nitrates by the action of lightning.

Nitrogen also moves through the ecosystem when carnivores like the lion eat herbivores like the eland.

Eland

Bacteria that live in soil or in the roots of peas, beans, and clover change nitrogen gas from the air into compounds that can be used by the plant to make proteins and hereditary material.

Perennial peanut roots

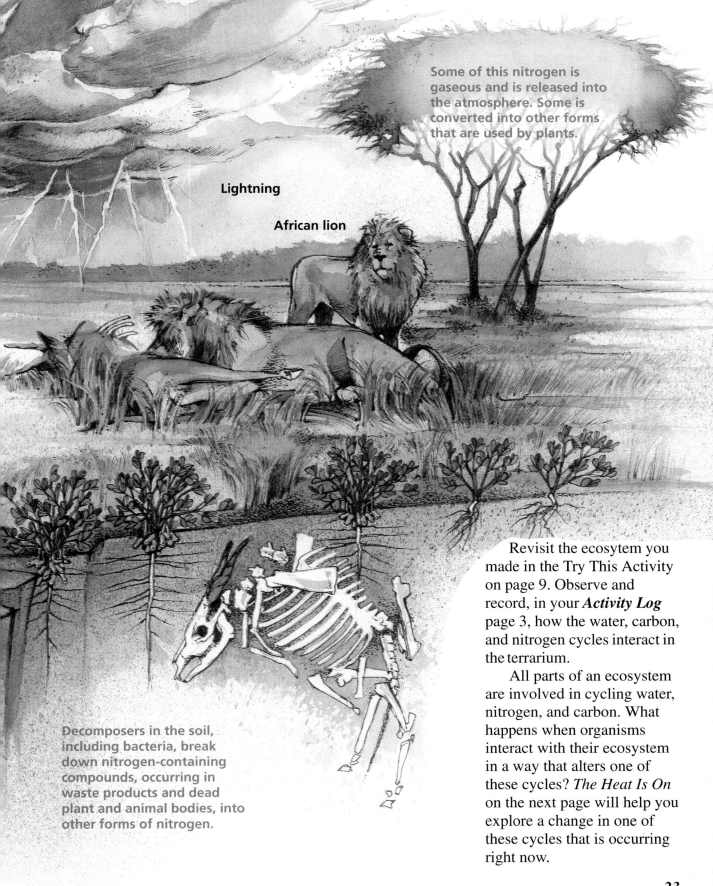

Some of this nitrogen is gaseous and is released into the atmosphere. Some is converted into other forms that are used by plants.

Lightning

African lion

Decomposers in the soil, including bacteria, break down nitrogen-containing compounds, occurring in waste products and dead plant and animal bodies, into other forms of nitrogen.

Revisit the ecosytem you made in the Try This Activity on page 9. Observe and record, in your *Activity Log* page 3, how the water, carbon, and nitrogen cycles interact in the terrarium.

All parts of an ecosystem are involved in cycling water, nitrogen, and carbon. What happens when organisms interact with their ecosystem in a way that alters one of these cycles? *The Heat Is On* on the next page will help you explore a change in one of these cycles that is occurring right now.

The Heat Is On

What would happen if the temperature where you live went up 10°—all year round? At first thought, if you live in a cold climate, you might like the idea of a warmer winter. However, this kind of temperature change could have some far-reaching effects on your environment and your life-style.

An "invisible" substance in our atmosphere has been causing the global temperature to rise. The average temperature of Earth, or average global temperature, has risen 0.4°C (1.1°F) in the last century.

Some scientists hypothesize that the global temperature will continue to rise over the next 50 to 100 years. It's still uncertain whether this will happen, but if the temperature continues to rise, the effects will be felt all over Earth. The distribution of rainfall and snowfall will change. As polar ice melts, the level of the oceans will rise. Growing seasons will change.

Scientists are paying special attention to the effects of global warming because change in the food-growing regions will affect world-wide food production. Some areas of Earth may experience longer growing seasons, but shorter growing seasons in others could produce severe food shortages. Humans may need to learn to depend on different foods altogether.

What is causing global temperatures to rise? Human activities such as driving cars, manufacturing goods, and cutting down rain forests increase the amount of carbon dioxide in the air. When fossil fuels such as coal, oil, and natural gas are burned, carbon dioxide is released. Using what you know about the carbon cycle, why might cutting down forests increase the amount of carbon dioxide in the air?

How might greater levels of carbon dioxide in the air contribute to global warming? Think about solar energy. When sunlight strikes Earth, much of the energy is absorbed by land and water warming the surface. Some, but not all, of this energy is then radiated back as heat from Earth to space. A simple way to visualize this process is to imagine the carbon dioxide as an insulating blanket above Earth that allows sunlight to pass through, but keeps much of the radiated heat in. The more carbon dioxide there is in the atmosphere, the thicker the blanket. As this trapped heat energy is absorbed by the atmosphere, the temperature rises.

Carbon dioxide forms an insulating blanket around Earth.

Minds On! What can we do about global warming? In groups of four to six, generate some ideas. What can you, your families, or friends do? What can be done, or needs to be done, globally? Select one person in the group to write these ideas down in his or her *Activity Log* on page 9. Then, do some individual research. Find out what solutions ecologists, engineers, physicists, agricultural scientists, or any other scientists around the world, are working on. Write a one- to two-page report on one area of research that interests you. Present it to the class. Then, discuss as a class what you can do about global warming. Share the lists from the group activity and draw on everyone's research.●

Some scientists hypothesize burning fossil fuels contributes to global warming.

◆　◆　◆　◆　◆

Sum It Up

The biotic and abiotic factors in an area make up an ecosystem with all parts of the ecosystem interacting. These factors interact to cycle water, carbon, and nitrogen through an ecosystem, ensuring that living organisms will have materials essential for growth. The abiotic factors—availability of nutrients, temperature, and water—determine which organisms can live in an ecosystem.

Using Vocabulary

abiotic factors
biotic factors
ecosystem

Using the vocabulary words, explain in a paragraph how biotic and abiotic factors interact in the ecosystem. Be sure that you have defined the terms clearly so someone who hasn't read this lesson would understand.

Critical Thinking

1. If all climates become warmer, what might the effect be on present-day ecosystems?
2. What does the word *cycle* mean and how is it related to water, carbon, and nitrogen?
3. What effect would the destruction of a large forest have on the cycling of matter?
4. How would the abiotic and biotic factors change in an ecosystem that has been flooded?
5. Fertilizers that contain nitrogen are often added to plants to help them grow. What step in the nitrogen cycle is being bypassed by adding fertilizers?

What Are Earth's Biomes?

ARE ALL TROPICAL RAIN FORESTS HOT AND HUMID? ARE ALL DESERTS ACROSS THE
WORLD HOT AND DRY? ENTER THE ECOLOGISTS' WORLD AND LEARN WHAT
DETERMINES WHERE ORGANISMS LIVE.

◆　◆　◆　◆　◆

The pictures on this page show different animals in their environments.
Lesson 1 described the three abiotic factors that primarily determine where
these organisms live—climate (light, temperature, and water), soil, and nutrients. Can you tell from the photos on these pages how the animals are suited to
live where they do? Try imagining each animal in the other environments—
does this give you any clues?

Minds On! How are the seal pup shown on this page and its environment
alike? Are the jackrabbit and its environment, the desert, alike in
any way? Do you see any similarities in the toucan (tü′ kan) and its environment? The fish and their environment? Why do you suppose these organisms
and their environments are alike? Write your explanation in your *Activity Log*
on page 10.●

What factors in each environment pictured always stay the same? The tropical rain forest, where the toucan lives, is always wet. Many of the factors in the
toucan's environment maintain a steady state that make it just right for this bird
to live there.

In this lesson you will learn about six different geographic areas on Earth
and two aquatic ecosystems, as well as the kinds of plants and animals that live
in them. You'll also make an imaginary journey to a tropical rain forest.

Can you predict the climate of the desert or the grasslands? What about
your environment? Do the following Explore Activity and determine the abiotic
factors common to six different land ecosystems.

Each animal is especially suited to its environment.

Activity!

What's the Weather Like?

You are about to explore the weather in six places around Earth without leaving the room. Since abiotic factors such as water and heat affect where organisms live, you will also begin to understand how plants and animals would have to be adapted to live in these six regions.

What You Need

1 red and 1 blue colored pencil
3 sheets of graph paper
Activity Log **pages 11–12**

What To Do

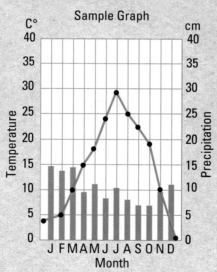

Sample Graph

to set up and complete your graphs. Label each graph with the name of one of the regions on the chart on page 29.

1 For this activity you need to make six graphs. Use two sheets of graph paper. Divide each sheet into fourths. You can use the extra two sections to make notes to yourself. Use the sample graph on this page as an example of how

2 With the red pencil, plot the information on temperature from the data table on the next page onto the first graph, as shown on the sample. Do this for each region, making a graph for all six.

3 With the blue pencil, and using the chart on precipitation, begin with the first graph and plot precipitation onto the graph paper for each region, as shown in the sample. Each graph will have precipitation and temperature graphed on it.

Use these data tables to graph temperature and precipitation.

PRECIPITATION (cm)						
Month	Region					
	Tundra	Taiga	Grassland	Deciduous forest	Desert	Tropical rain forest
January	1	2	3	13	3	28
February	1	2	3	12	3	28
March	0	2	6	13	2	33
April	1	1	9	9	1	29
May	1	2	12	10	1	18
June	2	2	12	8	1	10
July	3	3	9	10	0	5
August	3	6	12	8	1	4
September	3	7	8	7	0	6
October	2	5	6	7	2	12
November	1	2	5	9	2	15
December	0	2	4	11	2	20

TEMPERATURE (°C)						
Month	Region					
	Tundra	Taiga	Grassland	Deciduous forest	Desert	Tropical rain forest
January	−25	−10	−1	4	−1	25
February	−27	−8	2	5	2	24
March	−26	−6	6	10	6	25
April	−18	2	10	14	9	25
May	−4	8	16	18	10	25
June	2	12	22	23	14	25
July	6	14	26	28	18	25
August	6	12	25	25	18	25
September	3	8	22	22	16	26
October	−4	2	14	18	10	26
November	−16	−6	10	10	4	26
December	−24	−10	2	0	5	25

What Happened?

1. Briefly describe the climate in each region. What region does the sample graph show?
2. What do you think the major form of precipitation is for each region?
3. Where would you expect to find an organism that conserves water and disperses heat?
4. In which regions could an organism live that could not survive if the temperature fell below 4°C?

What Now?

1. What other abiotic factors besides temperature and precipitation make up the environment?
2. Why would it be unlikely that a desert would have the same organisms as a tropical rain forest?
3. Which one of these regions is most like the area where you live? Why? Which organisms are common in your area?
4. Would you expect that the plants or animals living in the land ecosystems react to light and temperature like the shrimp in the Explore Activity in Lesson 1 did?
5. Why do you think you were asked to plot the temperature and precipitation for each area?

EXPLORE

What Is a Biome?

The temperature and precipitation you plotted in the previous activity gave you a good idea of the climate for each of the six biomes on Earth. **Biomes** are communities of plants and animals in particular geographic areas of land with a distinct climate. **Climate** is the typical weather in a place over a long period of time, including precipitation, temperature, and seasonal patterns. One biome that you'll study in depth is the tropical rain forest.

Because environmental factors like climate affect organisms, any place on Earth that has precipitation and temperature typical of what you graphed for the tropical rain forest will have similar plants and animals.

Polar

Taiga

Tundra

Grassland

Desert

Deciduous forest

Tropical rain forest

World Biomes

60°

30°

Equator
0°

30°

60°

The abiotic factors present in the African grassland contribute to its unique and stable characteristics.

Why Are Biomes Found Where They Are?

To answer this question, we need to look at the reasons for the variations in climate over Earth.

The position a region has on Earth's surface is key to the temperature and kind and amount of precipitation that a region receives. You already know something about where you live on Earth's surface. What hemisphere do you live in? Is your home in a valley or on a mountain? Do you live near a lake or an ocean? These abiotic factors interact to produce the weather and eventually, climate, of a particular place.

Scientists and mapmakers use the terms *latitude* and *longitude* to describe a location on Earth. **Latitude** (lat′ i tüd′) is the distance north or south of the equator, measured in a unit called a degree. Longitude is the distance east and west as measured from pole to pole, beginning at the prime meridian. Latitude and longitude are not just lines on a map. They reflect information that is used to identify location and, in turn, to identify climates.

Minds On! If you know the latitude of a place, what else do you know about it? Compare what you know about temperatures at the equator with temperatures where you live. Write your answer in your ***Activity Log*** on page 13.●

In the Explore Activity on page 28, you used the temperature and precipitation graphs to identify the biome where you live and to estimate where on Earth each biome is located. The maps on pages 30 and 31 show the six major biomes on Earth and their climates. How close were your guesses? Where else does the kind of biome you live in exist? Notice that each continent has several biomes. How many biomes can you find on the continent of North America? On the continent of Africa?

Compare the biome of an area with its climate. How are they related?

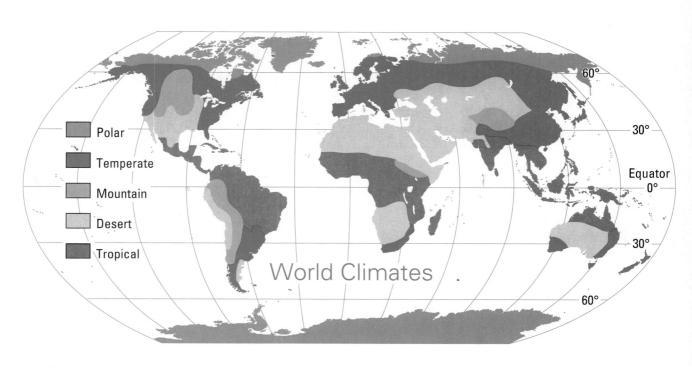

Polar
Temperate
Mountain
Desert
Tropical

World Climates

60°
30°
Equator 0°
30°
60°

Six Biomes—Many Locations

The six major biomes have differing temperature ranges and receive differing amounts of precipitation, but each biome can be found in a variety of locations.

Grassland
- ◆ **Location:** Mid-latitudes, interiors of continents
- ◆ **Climate:** Temperatures from 0°C–25°C; long, hot summers; irregular rainfall, 25 to 100 cm yearly
- ◆ **Plants:** Many species of grasses
- ◆ **Animals:** Grazing mammals; jackrabbits, gophers, lions

Taiga
- ◆ **Location:** Northern latitudes, south of tundra
- ◆ **Climate:** Winter as severe as tundra; summer temperatures warmer, 3–6 mon. growing season; 45–125 cm precipitation yearly
- ◆ **Plants:** Pines, smaller plants
- ◆ **Animals:** Long-legged hoofed animals, black bears, snowshoe hares

Tundra
- ◆ **Location:** Northern latitudes
- ◆ **Climate:** Winter temperatures below −40°C; summer temperatures as high as 10°C; 37 cm precipitation yearly; ground frozen most of the year
- ◆ **Plants:** Mosses, sedges, grasses
- ◆ **Animals:** Frequent white coloration

Desert
- **Location:** Near 30°N and 30°S latitudes, Africa, Asia, Australia, western North and South America
- **Climate:** From 10°C–38°C, hot days, cool nights; less than 10 cm rainfall yearly
- **Plants:** Cacti, creosote bush, mesquite
- **Animals:** Snakes, mice, camels, rabbits, birds

Deciduous Forest
- **Location:** Mid-latitudes of Northeastern and Southeastern U.S., Europe, parts of Japan, Australia
- **Climate:** Four distinct seasons; 75 to 250 cm precipitation yearly; rain and snow
- **Plants:** Deciduous trees
- **Animals:** Deer, black bears, squirrels, woodpeckers

Tropical Rain Forest
- **Location:** near equator
- **Climate:** Constant 25°C; high humidity, 200 cm yearly rainfall
- **Plants:** Wide variety
- **Animals:** Parrots and other birds, snakes, monkeys

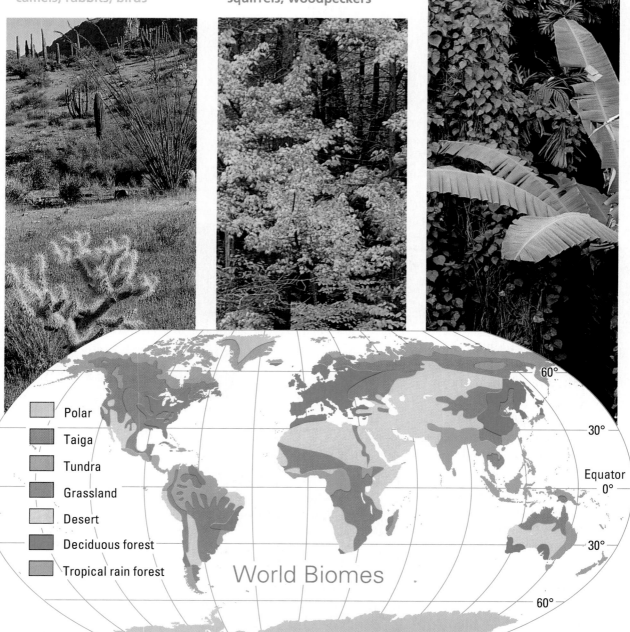

Polar
Taiga
Tundra
Grassland
Desert
Deciduous forest
Tropical rain forest

World Biomes

60°
30°
Equator
0°
30°
60°

Why do biomes like the tropical rain forest exist? The interactions of sunlight and geographical features, such as mountains and oceans, work together in an area to produce the climate's typical, stable pattern. Do you live in an area where the weather is very different in the winter and summer? If you have heavy snow in winter and hot humid summers, you know what to expect for each season. You know about how soon it will be warm enough to take the first swim of the year and when to expect the first snow. If you live around mountains, you know the weather in mountains is different from that in valleys, plains, or nearby desert. Some environments have the same weather most of the time, like the desert, where little rainfall is recorded all year. The graphs you made in the Explore Activity provide information about the climate in each biome. The climate tells you many things about the organisms that can live there.

Living and nonliving things interact in an environment. In a biome, the interaction of biotic and abiotic factors maintains the biome's stable, unique characteristics. For example, low rainfall and fire, which often spread over grasslands, pre-vent widespread tree growth. These abiotic factors maintain a typical characteristic of the grasslands—few trees.

Biomes are characterized by unique combinations of plants and animals. Although any one biome can be found in many places on Earth, wherever this biome occurs you find similar types of organisms living together. They live in the same environment because they require the same abiotic factors to survive—soil, temperature, or precipitation—or the same biotic factors.

Organisms in a biome interact with each other in various ways. Animals eat other organisms that also live in the biome. For example, animals such as cattle or buffalo are found in grasslands because they eat grass.

Plants and animals also compete with each other for light, water, and nutrients found in the environment. These interactions help give the biome its unique characteristics.

Do the next Try This Activity to explore what temperature has to do with a position on the surface of Earth.

Geographic locations situated near the same latitude often have similar climates.

Simpson Desert, Australia ▼

Kalahari Desert, Namibia, Africa ▶

Activity!

Solar-cooking Apples!

How does sunlight feel on your skin when you get up in the morning? How about at noon when Earth has moved and the sun is directly overhead? What do you think the sun will do to an apple left outside?

What You Need

2 large, recyclable foam cups
2 small, recyclable foam cups
2 8.5-in. by 11-in. sheets of aluminum foil
apple
scissors
masking tape
plastic wrap
rubber bands
2 sheets black construction paper
2 sheets white construction paper
***Activity Log* page 14**

Line two small cups with black paper, using tape to hold it in place. Cut two equal-sized pieces of apple, and put one slice in each small cup. Cover both cups

with plastic wrap and secure with a rubber band. Cover each sheet of white paper with aluminum foil. Then make a large cone out of this paper and foil combination. Fasten the cone with tape. Place one covered cup with an apple slice into the cone. Repeat the process for the second cup. Place each cone inside a large cup. Place one cup outside in the sun early in the morning—before 10 A.M. Angle the cup toward the sun. Record in your *Activity Log* how long it takes the apple to cook. Angle the second cup toward the sun at noon. Record in your *Activity Log* how long this apple takes to cook. Explain your results in your *Activity Log*.

As Earth rotates, the position of your home (and the apple slice) relative to the sun changes. Sunlight becomes more intense and then less intense as night falls. Why does the intensity of sunlight striking your home change during the day? The tilt of Earth's axis affects the hours and intensity of sunlight that a place receives. The more intense sunlight a place receives, the higher its average temperature will be. Average temperature falls as you move north or south of the equator to areas of higher latitude. Average temperature also falls as you move away from sea level into higher altitudes.

Did your apple slice cook faster at 10 A.M. or at noon? Provided no clouds filled the sky between 10 A.M. and noon and noon and completion, you probably found that the apple slices cooked more quickly at noon. What caused the cooking time to lessen the closer it got to noon? You know that the sun is supposed to be most directly overhead at noon. That means the rays are more direct, hotter, and better able to cook apple slices more rapidly.

Temperature is only one part of determining climate—precipitation is another part. Rain isn't the only form of precipitation. What form of precipitation falls in the tundra areas where seal pups live? What types of precipitation form in the area where you live—rain, snow, hail, sleet, dew, or fog? How much precipitation falls where you live?

Precipitation, like temperature, is related to latitude and altitude. It is also affected by geographic features, such as mountains and oceans.

Areas near 0° latitude generally receive heavy rainfall all year long. Because warm air can hold more moisture, these locations have not only rain but also humid conditions. Days at the equator are hot and humid in most places, and rain is common. If you have curly hair, it would be curlier in Central America. If you have straight hair, it would go limp in the high humidity. As you move away from the equator, the climate generally becomes drier.

Mountains affect precipitation by stopping clouds carrying moisture. The clouds release their moisture as rain on one side of the mountain, and the other side remains dry. Next to an ocean, air is moist from the evaporated ocean water. Coastal areas typically have more humidity than inland areas.

Mountain ranges affect climate, often creating areas on one side of the range with more-than-adequate precipitation and areas on the opposite side with a dry climate.

Minds On! A tropical plant called the *Victoria regia* water lily has leaves so large that they can support the weight of a child. Desert plants such as cacti have modified leaves called spines. At one stage in the water cycle, plants release water vapor through pores in their leaves. How would having a thick, waxy covering instead of a large, flat leaf enable some desert plants to conserve water? Why would desert plants, unlike tropical rain forest plants, need to conserve water? ●

Would water be released from the "leaves" of the *Victoria regia* water lily of the Amazon regions and the saguaro cactus of North America in differing amounts?

The emergent layer of the rain forest consists of trees that stand 10 to 20 meters (about 30 to 64 feet) above the canopy layer. These trees receive the most sun.

The canopy layer consists of trees 30 to 40 meters (about 100 to 130 feet) above the ground, so closely intertwined that there is no space between them.

The understory consists of large shrubs, small trees and vines struggling to reach the canopy layer, and palms that don't tolerate full sun.

Journey to a Tropical Rain Forest

Conserving the amount of water released from leaves would be a problem for plants in desert biomes. Plants in a tropical rain forest have large, flat leaves that allow larger amounts of moisture to be released into the air. You can tell from the biome map on pages 32 and 33 that rain forests cover only a small part of Earth's surface—less than seven percent. However, the tropical rain forest biome houses 50 to 70 percent of all species on Earth.

Tropical rain forests have distinct plant and animal life especially adapted to living in a hot, wet climate.

Imagine that you are making a journey to a tropical rain forest in South America. As soon as you enter the forest, you notice the high humidity. As much as 250 billion tons of water vapor can be suspended in the air at any one time in the rain forests of South America. Your pants and shirt feel wet from the high humidity. Rain is a daily occurrence. But here it's not just the humidity—it's also the heat.

Heat and moisture work together to maintain the rich variety of plant and animal life. When you were small, did you ever make a tent for yourself by covering chairs with blankets or towels? If so, you might remember that tent during your journey through the rain forest. When you look up and see a canopy of trees 35 to 45 meters (about 110 to 150 feet) tall, you note that the treetops almost block the sun, much as the blanket tent did. The light underneath the tropical rain forest canopy is dim and green in comparison to the brilliant sunshine you saw before you entered the forest. You hear parrots, toucans, and monkeys calling to each other in the canopy. At night, you hear the fluttering of bats as they move among the trees.

When you come upon a small clearing, you look up—more than 30 meters (about 100 feet) up—and notice that above the tree branches, intense sunlight is visible. You see one tree towering above the others, and, as you watch, a large bird swoops out of this tree, down into the dense treetops below it.

The illustration on these two pages shows five layers of plant life found in the rain forests. What is unique about each layer? Each layer is almost like a different environment. Which is sunny? Which will get more rain?

If you were flying over the forest, the tops of the trees would appear to be an emerald sea, with the trees of the emergent (or topmost) layer rising out of it. Harpy eagles and other birds live in these trees and feed on animals in the treetops below. Many species of beautifully colored butterflies flit in the brilliant sunshine over the tops of the trees.

The shrub layer consists of the smallest trees and large shrubs. These plants depend on sunlight that filters through the canopy and understory.

The herb layer is covered with several inches of decaying matter. Small plants and ferns grow here.

Most of the plants and animals that live in the rain forest live in the canopy layer. You would see a variety of monkeys; birds such as toucans, parrots, and hummingbirds; and reptiles such as the iguana and emerald tree boa. You might see colorful tree frogs and a large cat, the ocelot. Climbing vines called lianas (lē ä′ nəz) stretch from the forest floor up to the canopy layer, clinging to trees for support.

As you stand in the tropical rain forest, only patchy light hits you. The canopy is so dense it doesn't allow sun or much rain to pass through to the forest floor.

In the understory layer, you might see a tree porcupine walking along a branch. You might spy a sloth with green algae growing on its fur as it slowly moves upside down from tree to tree. Ferns and multicolored flowers, including orchids, grow on the trunks of trees, giving a fantasy-like feeling to the tropical rain forest.

Below the understory is a shrub layer, where the smallest trees and large shrubs grow. If the upper layers are dense, there won't be many plants in the shrub layer.

The canopy of the tropical rain forest is often shrouded in mists, a result of the biome's high humidity.

Algae that grows in the sloth's fur is an indicator of the high moisture content in the tropical rain forest biome.

Tiger beetle

Red-eyed tree frog

Small plants and ferns grow in shade in the herb layer on the forest floor. Even though the floor is usually covered by several inches of fallen leaves and decaying plant and animal matter, the soil underneath is not rich in mineral content. This is because nutrients are taken up by plants as soon as they become available. Many insects, including the scarab beetle, amphibians, such as the poison arrow frog, and mammals, such as the tapir and jaguar, live in the herb layer on the rain forest floor.

People also live on the forest floor—Native Americans like the Yanomamo (yä′ nō mä′mō) in Brazil have lived in the tropical rain forest for thousands of years, using its plentiful resources.

Plants and animals that live in the rain forest are all well-suited to life in a hot, humid environment. Many of them depend on each other for food, shelter, or assistance in reproducing, and couldn't live without each other. The plants and animals that live in the five other biomes are equally suited to their environment.

You may wonder about the plants and animals that live in a water environment. You may have noted that the six biomes listed are all land environments. Scientists classify aquatic environments differently since aquatic environments occur in every climate. A specific biome will occur in only one climate type. Scientists divide aquatic ecosystems into two major groups—freshwater ecosystems and marine ecosystems. Freshwater ecosystems include rivers and streams. Marine ecosystems are oceans and other salty bodies of water.

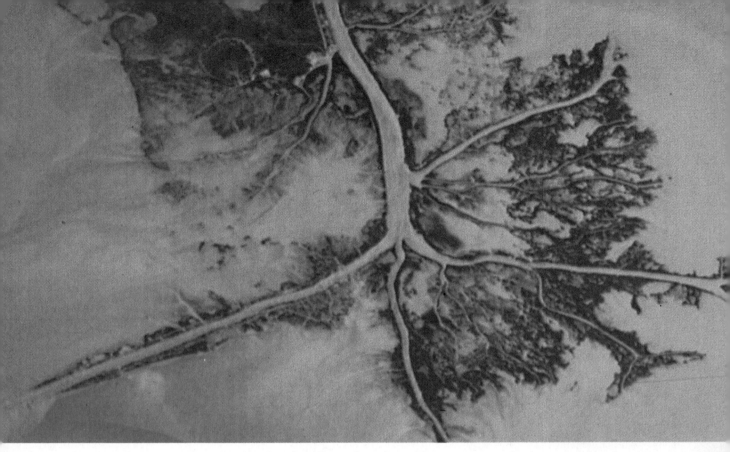

Estuaries, such as the Mississippi Delta, fragile ecosystems where rivers meet the ocean, teem with aquatic plant and animal life.

Freshwater Ecosystem

Freshwater and ocean areas take up the largest surface area of Earth, and many organisms live there. However, we identify these areas not as biomes but simply as aquatic ecosystems.

Perhaps there's a body of fresh water near where you live. If you follow a river downstream from its source to where it empties into another river, ocean, or lake, you'll notice certain changes as you travel. River water is often cold and fast-moving at its source. You might notice moss and algae growing on rocks in the water at the source. Perhaps you would see trout, salmon, or other fast-moving fish swim by.

Downstream, where the water moves more slowly, you would find fish such as carp, catfish, and bass, which move slowly, too. Eventually you come to an estuary. An **estuary** (ezs′ chü er′ ē) is the place where a body of fresh water meets the ocean. You see mudflats or salt marshes on either side of the water. You notice various forms of plant and animal life as well. Water birds, reptiles, and amphibians rely on estuaries as breeding grounds. Fish and mollusks use estuaries to breed and hatch young.

People also use estuaries. Because they provide a "seaside view," estuaries are prime locations for houses and apartment buildings. You already know that a change in one part of an ecosystem affects the stability of the whole. Building houses near estuaries can damage or

Activity!

What's in a Biome?

What You Need

cardboard shoe box
glue
pictures from magazines
colored pencils or markers
paper
***Activity Log* page 15**

Use the information you have gained from this lesson to build a model biome. Make a diorama that includes plants and animals that would be found in the biome you chose. Illustrate the climate conditions on the background. In your ***Activity Log*** write a paragraph about your model biome. Include factors such as climate, and major plants and animals. Imagine an organism that would be successful in this biome. Write a description of the organism's features that help it succeed. Include the factors of the biome the organism would thrive on. Illustrate your paragraph with your organism.

destroy the plant and marine life there. The ecosystem can no longer work to maintain a healthy state in an estuary when its banks are lined with condominiums. Water pollution, too, threatens the stability of estuaries by destroying the organisms that live in them. Estuaries receive all the water pollutants that are dumped upstream.

Literature Link

Swamps are freshwater ecosystems.

Seeds of Change

What ecosystem is something like a field full of water with trees growing in it that smells and makes weird noises? Swamps may resemble ponds gone wrong, but they are distinctive freshwater ecosystems, home to a variety of organisms. The Everglades National Park in Florida is an enormous swamp that has been preserved for its unique character and wildlife.

In the book *Seeds of Change* by Sarah Sargent,

you can explore a swamp ecosystem in Georgia along with Rachel.

Rachel's father planned to develop a theme park in the swamp. Development of this kind has both pros and cons. After listing the pros and cons of swamp development, draw a conclusion based upon what you have learned about ecosystems and changes within them. Write a brief paragraph explaining why you think the theme park should be built or why it shouldn't.

Where organisms live in the ocean depends on the light source they require. Algae, a photosynthetic organism of this ecosystem, and the simple organisms and tiny animals like brine shrimp that eat algae, live in the well-lighted waters at the surface of the ocean and near shores. Small fish such as herrings also live in this part of the ocean and eat these small plants and animals. Along shores, mammals such as seals, sea otters, or walruses, and birds such as gulls, sandpipers, or penguins can be found feeding on ocean life. Shellfish such as crabs, barnacles, and oysters live in tidal pools, on rocks, or on the bottom near shore.

Deeper in the ocean live larger fish that feed on smaller fish or the plankton that fall from the surface. Whales, octopi, jellyfish, and porpoises are just a few of the animals that live below the surface level. Many of the organisms that live in this part of the ocean can also rise and fall to other levels. Whales and porpoises can even leap out of the water.

Some organisms live deep in the ocean where light can't penetrate. They feed on dead organisms that fall from above. Many, like the viper fish, have adapted to the dark over many years by evolving

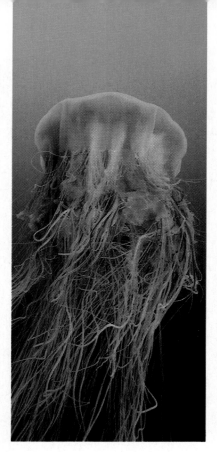

Jellyfish live just below the ocean's surface.

the ability to make their own light, which attracts prey! Others have feelers that help them detect food falling through the water.

Frequently things we use every day come from biomes that we will never experience. In the Minds On that follows, you will be asked to examine your surroundings for things foreign to your biome.

Minds On! Plants you see on occasion and nonliving things you use every day may come from a biome or ecosystem far away from the biome where you live. In this Minds On you will identify and name the biomes and ecosystems of some familiar objects.

Go through your home, classroom, or nearby store, and list organisms, or items made by organisms, from any biome other than the one in which you live, or from an aquatic ecosystem. Look in your refrigerator, cupboard, or closet for ideas. Ask your family or friends for ideas. Consider plants as possibilities. In your *Activity Log* on page 16, identify the biome or ecosystem for each item that you list. How did you determine which items were from other biomes? Can you tell by observing how an organism, such as a houseplant, was adapted to its native biome?●

You may have been surprised as to where some everyday objects came from. Did anyone consider the fish you ate last week? The fish may have come from a marine ecosystem if it was an ocean fish like flounder or snapper. You may also be surprised to find out that people are actually farming marine fish in areas that do not have a naturally occurring marine environment. Read the Focus on Technology feature that follows to see how a marine ecosystem is being used to feed people.

These frames hold oysters cultivated in this Washington state seabed.

Farming Fish Is Catching On

A marine ecosystem produces a rich variety of foods, not only for other marine organisms but also for land organisms. Because humans consider fish such a good food source, over-harvesting has occurred in some areas. One solution to the problem is to grow fish, much like farmers grow cattle or corn.

Aquaculture, or fish farming, a highly developed industry in Asia and South America, is "catching on" in the United States. Traditional fishing methods can no longer yield enough fish to meet world demand. Moreover, water pollution has damaged or destroyed many traditional fishing grounds.

Fish that live in water polluted by sewage or runoff from industrial wastes are unsafe to eat. Aquaculture allows humans to produce more fish and healthier fish that are easily obtained.

Most of the oysters that Americans consume are cultured, or planted, in ocean waters. But aquafarming isn't limited to marine areas. In landlocked Utah, lobster farmers breed and grow these crustaceans in saltwater-filled raceways. In Texas a power plant does double duty by raising catfish in water used for cooling equipment. Aquaculture will work wherever humans create an environment that has what a fish population needs to survive.

Humans Affect Biomes

Change in one part of an ecosystem affects the entire ecosystem since all parts of an ecosystem interact. Whether the change comes from abiotic factors or biotic factors, the change still affects the entire ecosystem. Humans have been responsible for great changes in ecosystems. People affect Earth's biomes with activities such as planting and harvesting trees, building housing, and burning fossil fuels. Some human activities have decreased the ability of biomes to sustain life.

South American countries are experiencing great population growth. More and more tropical rain forests are being cut down to provide space for agriculture and cattle ranching to feed growing populations. North Americans have a part in the rain forest changes—beef produced by cattle ranching on land that once was tropical rain forest is purchased in North American markets.

Unfortunately, clearing tropical rain forests has many negative consequences. Much of what is true for the South American rain forests is also true for the tropical rain forests of Asia, Africa, Australia, and New Zealand. The easiest way to clear a section of forest is to burn it. Most of

the nutrients in a rain forest are held in the trees, not in the soil. Burning trees creates a nutrient-rich ash that is a good fertilizer. But even with the nutrient-rich ash, farming on this land can produce only a few harvests before the land "wears out" and more land needs to be cleared. Living trees and other plants on the forest floor help prevent erosion. Without them, soil is eroded and washed away. Without the continuous cycling of decaying matter from organisms, nutrients in

the soil are quickly depleted.

Reduction of tropical rain forests also concerns ecologists because of the plant-global warming connection you studied in Lesson 1. Burning reduces the number of trees in the tropical rain forest. It also adds carbon dioxide to the atmosphere. Since there are fewer plants after the burning, there are fewer plants to use up the carbon dioxide and fewer plants to release oxygen. The carbon cycle is affected. Scientists hypothesize that reducing the

Acres of South American rain forests are often cleared by burning.

The Yanomamo of Brazil have lived in the rain forests for hundreds of years. Clearing tropical rain forests sometimes takes away land occupied by these people. How would this affect their population and life-style? Does the tropical rain forest belong to the Yanomamo? People like the Yanomamo have learned to adapt to the tropical rain forest. They hold knowledge of how to use the plants in a variety of ways— because they've been doing so for hundreds of years. When their culture is changed, the traditional knowledge will be lost as well.

While the preservation of the tropical rain forests is a "burning issue" for many ecologists, conservation of all forests is important for ecological stability. The size of North American forests has been reduced since settlers first appeared. Read the two links on the next page for a North American slant to the effects of humans on biomes.

number of forests will increase the thickness of the carbon dioxide blanket encircling Earth and contribute to global warming.

The dense vegetation of the tropical rain forest contains more species than any other land biome. Scientists have just begun to study the organisms that live within the tropical rain forests. As tropical rain forests are destroyed, it is possible that many of the species adapted to life there will become extinct.

Consider this—many tropical plants recently "discovered" by scientists but known to the peoples living in the tropical rain forests, can be used as medicines. Extracts from the bark of one of the trees have long been used to fight malaria, a mosquito-borne sickness common in hot, wet climates. Scientists have begun to use other plants to fight cancer, leukemia, and muscular and heart diseases.

Forester

Good things are happening in the environment, too. Forester Ann Genovese of Washington state has had a part in restoring forests destroyed by the 1980 eruption of Mt. Saint Helens.

After the eruption, Ann and her team of foresters took samples of the soil in the volcanic area and evaluated the growth rate of trees and other plants in the area of the eruption. They also quickly planted thousands of acres with seedlings.

Ann also studies tree harvesting methods, trying to determine the ones that allow faster replanting—an attempt to meet people's needs for forest products without upsetting the equilibrium of the forest.

Foresters like working outdoors and finding new ways to improve old methods. Most foresters attend college and many hold advanced degrees. You can get more information about forestry as a career by writing to:

> USDA Forest Service
> P.O. Box 96090
> Washington, DC 20090-6090.

Forester Ann Genovese works to repair damage to existing forests.

Language Arts  Link

Spotted Owl vs. Logging

The northern spotted owl, a regal bird that stands about 45 centimeters (17 to 18 inches) tall and is so trusting it will eat from your hand, is in danger. The spotted owl lives in the forests of the Pacific coast of North America, from British Columbia to San Francisco, and in the Rocky Mountains from Colorado into Mexico. But the number of spotted owls is rapidly decreasing. People are steadily destroying this species by logging the ancient fir trees where the owl lives.

Every change in an ecosystem affects the ecosystem as a whole. The 200-year-old trees in the forests where the spotted owl lives interact with other environmental factors to clean the air, regulate water levels, and enrich the soil. Without the trees, the forest ecosystem can't be maintained as it is. Some

Northern Spotted Owl

people argue that logging in forests where the spotted owl lives should be severely restricted. Other people point out that restricting logging would put lumberjacks and paper mill employees out of work. Almost everyone agrees there's a problem in the spotted owl's home.

What do you think? Should logging in forests where the spotted owl lives be restricted? Write a newspaper editorial that expresses your opinion and gives reasons to support it.

◆ ◆ ◆ ◆ ◆

Sum It Up

Sunlight and geography interact to produce a regional climate. Because organisms interact with their physical environment, climate and nutrient availability determine the distribution of organisms on Earth. Biomes are stable ecosystems that contain characteristic plant and animal life. There are six major land biomes and two aquatic ecosystems on Earth. The tropical rain forest covers only seven percent of Earth's land area, but nearly 70 percent of Earth's plant life is found there. Destruction of the world's forests may result in worldwide climate changes.

Using Vocabulary

biomes   **climate**   **estuary**   **latitude**

You are an *environmentalist* working near a marine environment that is being threatened because too many houses, apartments, and hotels are being built. It's a beautiful area, home to not only seals but also sea otters and a variety of marine birds. The latest housing development is going to be built at the mouth of the Slate River as it empties into the ocean. Write a paragraph explaining what you think should be done with the development, making sure you include the four vocabulary words from Lesson 2. Be sure that those words, by explanation, are clear to someone who has not read Lesson 2.

Critical Thinking

1. Why does the tropical rain forest support the greatest diversity of life found in the six biomes?

2. If the climate in a grassland changed and 100 centimeters of rain began to fall each year, what changes would you expect to see in the area over a 15- to 20-year period?

3. Where in the ocean would you expect to find the most fish? Why?

4. What are the consequences of estuaries being destroyed in order to build housing?

5. How does the destruction of tropical rain forests affect people who live in other biomes?

How Many

Are There?

POPULATIONS CHANGE OVER TIME. WHAT FACTORS AFFECT THE PATTERNS OF CHANGE IN A POPULATION?

◆   ◆   ◆   ◆   ◆

Elephants live in one ecosystem. California poppies live in another. Bamboo is found in yet another. Each has different needs for survival and can be found where those needs can be met.

Groups of the same kind of organism are often found living close to each other. In the photographs on these pages, the geese flock together, the poppies grow on the same hillside, and bamboo clumps together. What kind of organisms live in your environment?

Minds On! What plants or animals live in groups in your neighborhood? List them in your *Activity Log* on page 17. Why might the number of organisms in each group increase or decrease?●

You probably named quite a few groups, from ants to sparrows to dandelions. Did you use a forest of trees as an example of a group of organisms living in your neighborhood?

Sometimes the number of organisms in your neighborhood decreases because of you. If you heard the hum of a mosquito and saw it hovering over your arm, the action you would take would decrease the number of mosquitoes in your neighborhood.

In this lesson you will learn about the patterns of change, or variations, in the size of groups of organisms like those you have just seen and thought about. Ecologists take special interest in populations of organisms. Increases or decreases in plant and animal populations give clues to changes in an environment. In the Explore Activity that follows, you will use a technique for counting populations that ecologists use.

Each environment has organisms common to it—from elephants to poppies, from geese to bamboo.

Activity!

How Many Live Here?

The number of dandelions in a lawn, ants in your neighborhood, or elephants in the world may increase or decrease, but how do we know? Sometimes the number of organisms in a group is so small they can be counted, like dandelions in a lawn. Other groups are too large to count, like the ants; so the number of ants must be estimated. In this Explore Activity you'll explore one way to count the number of individuals living in the same area.

What You Need

4 stakes
meter tape
string
Activity Log **pages 18–19**

What To Do

1 Go to the area your teacher has assigned. Randomly select a starting point.

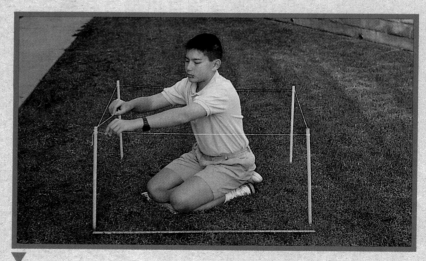

2 Use the meter tape to measure a square 1 m on each side. Place a stake at each corner of the square, and tie a string around the stakes.

3 Turn to the square in your *Activity Log*. Diagram to scale any physical features such as rocks, trees, or pavement that happen to be in the sample plot.

animals are present, count those as well. Mark on your diagram where they were found.

6 Repeat step 5 until you have counted and mapped the four sections.

7 Total the numbers of each kind of plant or animal counted in your plot.

8 Copy the data from each group of students in your class into Table 2 in your ***Activity Log***. Note the number of groups you have.

9 Divide the total number of each type of organism (the totals from Table 2) by the number of groups that are listed in the table. These numbers are the average numbers of each type of organism per 1-m square in the areas you sampled. Record these averages in your ***Activity Log*** for each organism.

4 To count the plants accurately, divide the plot into four 50-cm square sections. Lay the meter tape along one side and a piece of string across the plot 50 cm from the outside edge. Place the second string across the first, 50 cm from the edge.

5 Count the number of each type of plant in the first 50-cm square section. Record the numbers in Table 1 in your ***Activity Log***. Using a different symbol for each plant, map the plants on the diagram in your ***Activity Log***. If any

What Happened?

1. List each plant in your plot, and tell whether it was more or less common than the class average.
2. How were the organisms distributed in the plot? Was this different than the plots your classmates studied?
3. If you saw insects or evidence of animals, what were they doing there?

What Now?

1. Did you observe anything that would account for the differences between the numbers of plants in your plot and the class averages?
2. What are some factors that might make the number of plants or animals go up or down if you sampled the same area next week or next month?
3. Why is the class average a better estimate of the number of plants or animals in an area than just one plot?

EXPLORE

Counting Populations

A **population** is all the organisms of the same species that live in an area. All the humans in the world, all the oak trees on a lawn, and all the orchids in a tropical rain forest make up different populations. In the Explore Activity, you identified how many different kinds of plants live in a one-meter square plot, or the number of different populations there were. You also counted how many of each plant lived there or the size of each population.

When organisms are large and there aren't too many of them, such as oak trees on a lawn, scientists can easily count them by looking at them. You directly counted the numbers of organisms in your plot. However, counting the numbers of individuals in a population isn't always easy. Suppose a field mouse moves in and out of an area where a scientist is trying to determine the field mouse population. The mouse may be counted twice—once on its way into the area and again on its way out. A fast-moving

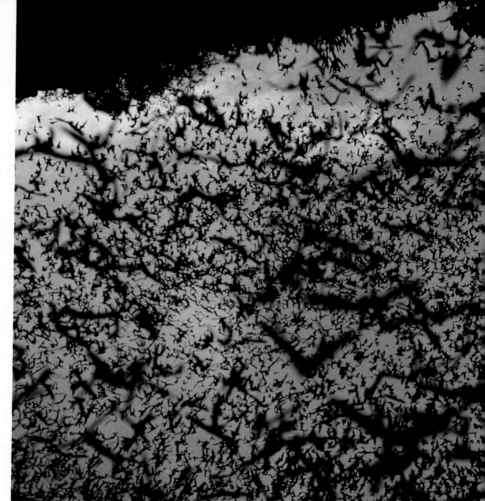

field mouse may escape the scientist's notice altogether.

Did you see animals or evidence of animals in your plot? Think about the living creatures you could *not* see. Could there have been anything living in the soil or under rocks or pavement? Some organisms living there are too small to be seen without a microscope.

Scientists have developed ways to ensure that variables such as stray mice don't prevent them from obtaining an accurate count. One method of estimating the population

of animals in an area is to capture and mark some of the animals with ear tags, leg bands, or dye. The marked animals are then released. Next, the scientists randomly capture a second group of animals in the same area. Some of the animals that were marked in the first group will be in the second group, too. The scientists then calculate the percentage of marked animals in the second group of animals captured. From this percentage, they can estimate the total population in the area.

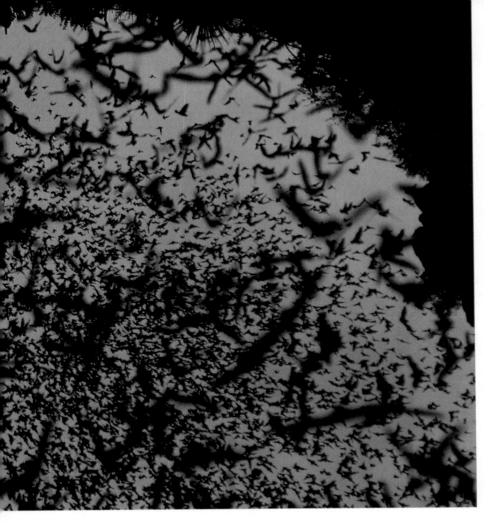

Revisit the ecosytem you made in the Try This Activity on page 9. Observe and record, in your *Activity Log* page 3, how you counted the population of the organisms in the terrarium. Are there any new organisms? Are there any populations that have declined?

Videotaping the bats at Carlsbad Caverns helps calculate population density.

Another more "high-tech" method scientists can use to ensure accuracy in counting moving animals is videotaping. To estimate the population of Mexican free-tailed bats in Carlsbad Caverns, New Mexico, scientists videotaped the bats at dusk against the blue sky as they flew out of the cave where they live. The scientists then used a computer program to count the number of bats in each frame of the videotape.

We can learn a lot about different organisms by counting populations.

Exterminators estimate the termite population in an infested house to determine how much insecticide they must use to eliminate the termites. Scientists count populations of species such as the spotted owl to determine whether the species is endangered and should be protected. Ecologists count different species of fish in a lake to find out how acid rain or industrial pollution is affecting the organisms that live there.

A field scientist in Costa Rica helps count the sea turtle population.

Population Density

When you calculated the number of plants or animals per square meter in your Explore Activity, you were calculating the population density of the area. **Population density** is the number of individuals per unit of living space in an environment. If you had sampled a tropical rain forest, the emergent trees would have had a low population density, maybe two or three trees per hectare (2.471 acres). The density of trees in the canopy layer of the rain forest would be much greater.

Population density can vary from place to place. Within the plot you explored in the activity, the populations were greater in some sections than others. Groups of your classmates sampled different plots in an area. The density of any plant probably varied among the plots. Could you identify any patterns in the way the organisms were distributed?

There is a pattern in the population density of trees in the rain forest, too. There are more trees in the canopy layer than in the understory and few trees in the emergent layer.

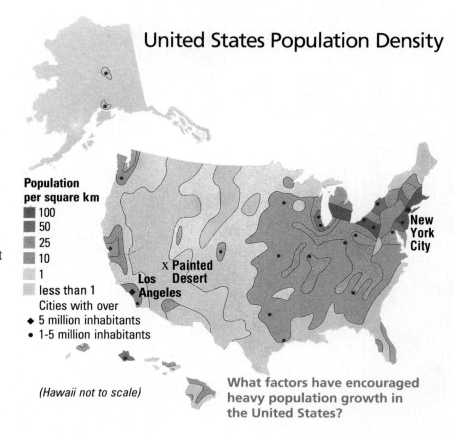

Population per square km
- 100
- 50
- 25
- 10
- 1
- less than 1

Cities with over
- ◆ 5 million inhabitants
- • 1-5 million inhabitants

(Hawaii not to scale)

X Painted Desert
Los Angeles
New York City

What factors have encouraged heavy population growth in the United States?

The map on this page shows the human population density of the United States. Notice the high population density of New York City. Now locate the Painted Desert on the map. Is the human population density there higher or lower than in New York City? Do you see a pattern in the way people are distributed in the United States?

Minds On! In your *Activity Log* on page 20, list some reasons why you think human population is distributed as it is on the map.●

All populations fall into one of three patterns. The individuals are either spread out evenly, unevenly, or in clumps. The most common pattern of the three is clumping.

Think about the lunchroom at your school. In what pattern is the population of students usually distributed there? Suppose students were spread out rather than clumped in the lunchroom. Would students enjoy lunchtime more or less? Students are clumped in the lunchroom by groups of friends. Students who go to the same school often live in clumps—in the same area of a city. People who work in certain industries, such as the auto industry or the movie industry, are often clumped in certain parts of the United States, like Detroit or Hollywood.

Clumping happens when organisms form groups for protection, to help one another, or because resources such as water or food (or jobs) are concentrated in one spot. Some birds protect each other while in flocks by giving warning cries when danger approaches. Kittens may huddle together when they sleep to keep warm. Wolves in a pack help each other by hunting for food together. Cottonwood trees grow along streams or rivers in grasslands because a resource they need —water—is found there.

Even spacing is the second most common pattern in which populations are distributed. The picture on this page shows a plant called a creosote (krē ə sōt′) bush. Creosote bush populations are evenly spaced. In the poor, dry soil of the desert, creosote bushes need to be far away from each other in order to acquire all the resources they need to survive. The roots of the creosote bush produce chemicals that keep other creosote bushes from germinating close enough to compete for water and nutrients.

The least common pattern of population distribution is uneven spacing. Trees and other plants in tropical rain forests come close to being unevenly spaced. There's no benefit for them if they group around water sources, or compete for water, because water and nutrient-rich leaves fall in abundance over the surface of the soil. There is no need for them to help each other in any way. The distribution is almost random, without any pattern.

Populations of birds clump together for protection.

Even spacing allows creosote bushes enough nutrients for survival.

Trees and plants within the tropical rain forest grow in an uneven spacing pattern.

Variations in Population Size

Remember why populations such as field mice are hard to count? Field mice are often on the move. Isn't that true about the population of the United States? Individuals in this population are also often on the move. Did you, your relatives, or ancestors come from a different country to the United States? Has anyone you know ever moved to another country? Migration—moving into or out of an area—causes changes in the size of populations.

What happens to a mosquito hovering over your arm if you swat the mosquito and miss? Nothing. But if you swat and hit the mosquito, the mosquito dies. The mosquito population decreases. What happens to the dog population if you allow your dog to have puppies? It increases. Birth and death cause changes in the size of populations.

When your parents encourage you to eat nutritious foods such as skim milk, green vegetables, and citrus fruits, they point out that these foods make you healthier and help you grow. What if every boy and girl on Earth ate only nutritious foods? The human population would grow, because we would all be healthier and could live longer. Nutrition is one of the factors that affects the growth of organisms.

When provided with ideal conditions for growth and reproduction, including abundant light, heat, water, nutrients, and freedom from disease or accident, almost any organism will experience a rapid increase in its population. Under ideal conditions, the larger in size a population becomes, the faster it grows. The number of individuals that could be produced in a population under the best possible conditions is its *biotic potential*.

POPULATION SIZE

0   **TIME**

In calculating biotic potential, the British scientist Charles Darwin estimated that a pair of elephants could have 19 million descendents after 750 years.

Overpopulation of wildebeests in Kenya, Africa, has resulted in overgrazing and an eventual decrease in the population.

Populations don't usually increase in number as rapidly as the elephants Darwin estimated. In "real life," populations do not realize their biotic potential because conditions are almost never ideal. A **limiting factor** is a condition that prevents a population from reaching its biotic potential. The lack of any resource, such as food, light, or water, that a population needs to survive, grow, or reproduce is a limiting factor. It may affect the population by decreasing the birth rate or increasing the death rate.

A population may also decrease suddenly as a result of disease or natural disasters. Disease caused by insects can destroy your vegetable garden, but you can also destroy the insect population with insecticides. Draining a swamp that provided a home for fish and birds will decrease the populations of both. Have you ever experienced a late frost in the spring that killed fruit blossoms, a summer drought that killed farmers' crops, or a severe storm that flooded a valley, killing all the vegetation in its path? The 1988 forest fire at Yellowstone National Park destroyed much of the population of trees in the park. The eruption of Mount Vesuvius (və sü′ vē əs) wiped out the ancient Italian city of Pompeii (pom pā′) in A.D. 79, killing most of the population of 20,000.

What do you suppose happens to the size of a population if the changes due to birth and migration are equal to the changes due to death and emigration? The population stabilizes, or stays the same, at a level called carrying capacity. **Carrying capacity** is the maximum population size that the resources in an area, such as water, light, and food, can support. Carrying capacity is different from biotic potential. While biotic potential is the number of individuals that could be produced in a population under the best possible conditions—unlimited resources available—the carrying capacity is the maximum population size that can be supported by existing conditions in an area—usually not ideal.

What happens in a population as it grows toward its carrying capacity? How is it different from a small population in the same ecosystem? Do the Try This Activity on the next page to observe the difference.

Activity!

Move Over!

Do plants squeezed for space and competing for the same nutrients grow as well as those with room to spare? In this activity you'll compare two groups of marigold plants growing under the same conditions. The only variable between the two is the size of the population of marigold plants. Observe the effect population size has on individual plants.

What You Need

50 marigold seeds, 2 milk cartons, scissors, potting soil, measuring cup, masking tape, pen, water, *Activity Log* page 21

Cut the tops off 2 milk cartons, and label them A and B, using the masking tape. Fill each planter with the same amount of potting soil, measuring with the cup. Plant 10 marigold seeds in planter A and 40 in planter B. Place them in a sunny place. Water the soil whenever it seems dry, but always water both planters at the same time. Measure the amount of water you give them, and give the same amount to each. When the sprouts are 3 cm high, record the number of sprouts in each planter in your *Activity Log*. Every other day for 10 to 15 days, record how the plants look in your *Activity Log*. Compare your results with those of your classmates. Explain the differences between planters A and B in your *Activity Log*. What abiotic and biotic factors produced the results?

Math 🔲 Link

What Percent of the Ecosystem?

In the Explore Activity, you determined population sizes in a region—but you also determined the number of populations in this environment. Which plant species was the most common, or accounted for the greatest percentage of the total plants in your sample? Ecologists calculate the percent of organisms in an environment. For example, certain fish are killed easily by water pollution. As they are killed off, other hardier fish may take their place. When percentages of fish change in a lake, it may be a sign that the lake is being polluted. The presence of earthworms in soil can be an indication of the health of an ecosystem because toxins in soil kill earthworms.

Using the data you collected in the Explore Activity on pages 52 and 53, calculate the percentage of total plants for each species of plant. For example, if a plot in a field had 25 daisies out of 100 plants, the percentage of daisies would be 25 percent.

The percentage of earthworms in soil gives an indication to the healthiness of the ecosystem.

Could you hypothesize which marigold would grow the best from what you know about populations and resources needed for survival?

In the 1950s a popular game on many college campuses involved finding out how many people could be stuffed into a telephone booth. As long as there was even the tiniest amount of available space in the booth, students would try to fit another person inside. There was no more space when no amount of squeezing together would enable another person to come in. The environment of the telephone booth could not hold another individual.

Any environment has a limit to the number of individuals it can physically hold. However, even if space in an ecosystem isn't filled, there is a limit to the resources, such as food, water, and light, that it contains. As the size of the population approaches the carrying capacity of its environment, more resources will be consumed, and they will become harder to obtain. The two populations of marigold plants you grew in the Try This Activity on the previous page were using the same amount of resources—space, soil, water, and light. But one population was sharing the resources among many more individuals. What would have happened if you had had twice as many marigold plants in the crowded planter? As the population approaches carrying capacity, individuals will compete with each other to get scarce resources. The death rate rises and the birth rate declines because the conditions for growth and reproduction are not good. In addition, diseases spread more rapidly in an environment that is densely populated, increasing the death rate.

CARRYING CAPACITY OF ENVIRONMENT

NUMBER OF ORGANISMS

POINT OF MAXIMUM GROWTH

0

TIME →

As the population reaches carrying capacity, growth slows because many individuals are competing for scarce resources.

Human Population Growth

Like every population, humans encounter limiting factors. **Limiting factors** are conditions in the environment that keep a population from increasing in size. Humans have overcome limiting factors many times during our history, allowing our population to expand again and again. The timeline on this page shows the growth of the human population from the beginning of human history to the present. The discovery of fire and invention of tools and weapons allowed early humans to protect themselves from enemies and to acquire food more effectively. The development of agriculture and the domestication of animals around 8000 B.C. provided a more dependable food supply. The development of industry in the 18th century increased the food supply for humans even further. Scientific discoveries led to the

▲ **Earthquake, Armenia**

production of vaccines and drugs that have almost wiped out many life-threatening diseases such as tuberculosis. Midwives and doctors have helped mothers deliver healthier babies, and the number of women who die in childbirth has decreased. Builders and architects have designed homes and apartment buildings that can help protect us from natural disasters such as floods and earthquakes.

As we have reduced limiting factors like disease and increased the amount of food available, the human population has grown tremendously.

It took more than one million years for the population of humans in the world to reach one billion. In only 100 years after that, it doubled to two billion people, and 45 years later it doubled to four billion. In 11 more years, world population reached five billion. Currently, the human population of the world grows at more than 89 million each

▲ **Flooding,**   **Volcanic activity,** ▶
United States   **United States**

year—one million people are born every four days. Some people have asked what will happen when the human population reaches carrying capacity. Some people have taken steps to slow down population growth. Some believe it is not a problem of overpopulation but one of distribution. Read the Social Studies Link on page 64 and examine limiting factors in human population growth.

Human Population Timeline

Limiting factors such as wars, disease, and natural disasters affect human population growth.

▼ *Development of agriculture*

| 8000 B.C. | 7000 B.C. | 6000 B.C. | 5000 B.C. | 4000 B.C. |

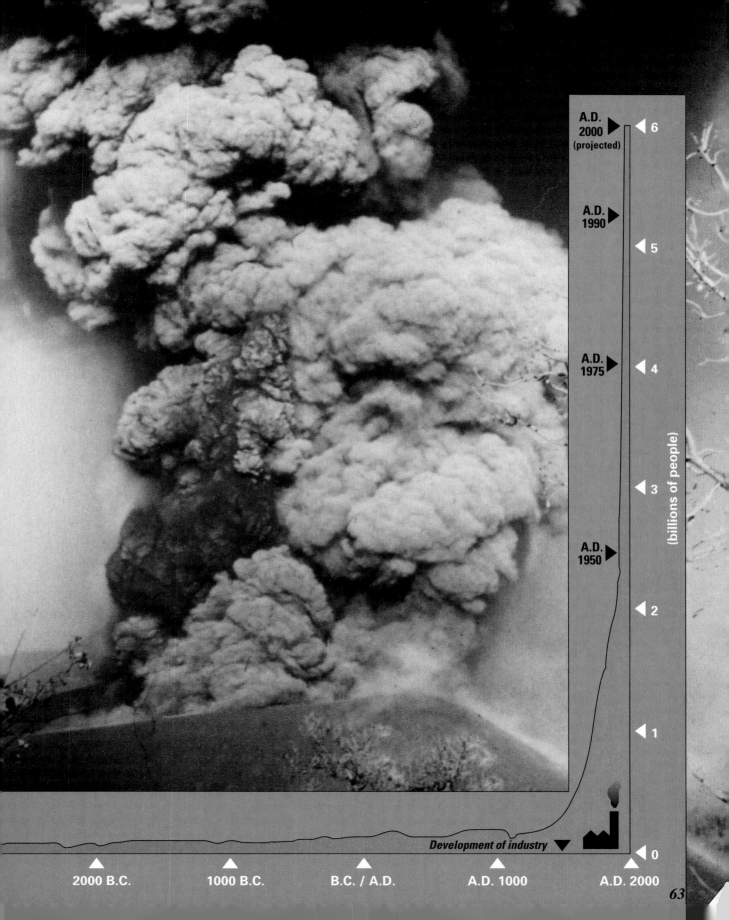

A.D.
2000
(projected) ▶ ◀ 6

A.D.
1990 ▶
          ◀ 5

A.D.
1975 ▶ ◀ 4

          ◀ 3

A.D.
1950 ▶

          ◀ 2

(billions of people)

          ◀ 1

Development of industry ▼
          ◀ 0

2000 B.C.   1000 B.C.   B.C. / A.D.   A.D. 1000   A.D. 2000

63

Some Have Too Much, Some Too Little

What is the carrying capacity of Earth for humans? Most scientists hypothesize that Earth has enough resources to support its 5.3 billion humans, but, at present, this is not happening. You know that populations are distributed in different patterns. Resources are distributed on Earth, and within populations, in different patterns. In some countries, including the United States, most people have much more food than they need. Americans often become malnourished not from lack of food but from eating "junk food" snacks instead of nourishing meals. Such problems are unthinkable in countries such as Ethiopia (ē thē ō′ pē ə) and regions such as the Sahel (sə hil′) in Africa where thousands of people go hungry or die from lack of food every day. Even here in the United States, however, some people don't have enough to eat or a place to sleep at night. Part of the problem in some areas of the world is that food that could be used to feed people is simply not distributed, due to government inefficiency or apathy.

In groups of three or four, research the problem of unequal distribution of resources on Earth. Share your solutions in a whole-class discussion.

CAREERS

Demographer

How many textbooks will be needed in Guatemala in five years? Will this year's projected crop be adequate to feed the population of Somalia? How will the summer's drought affect the food supply in the United States?

Ruby Garcia is a demographer who has an inside track on how human populations are affected by limiting factors such as food, overcrowding, and illness. She has recently returned from a trip to Togo, a country in west Africa, to gather information on the size, location, growth, and distribution of populations there for the government.

According to Ruby, a demographer is made of parts—she works as a geographer, sociologist, mathematician, policy planner, and computer scientist all rolled into one career.

Once Ruby has the information gathered, she enters it into a computer. The accumulated data is then analyzed. From that analysis, Ruby recommends to governmental agencies what course they should take. She has advised governmental agencies on environmental policies, noting trends. She was recently part of an advisory committee that studied the increase of homelessness and poverty among children, suggesting governmental policy changes that might ease the problems.

Ruby did not decide in high school that she would become a demographer. After studying sociology in college, she then continued her higher education. Some demographers choose this career after studying other related areas.

If you have a curiosity about why things are the way they are and you like numbers as well as people, you might consider life as a demographer. For further information about a career in demography, write:

The Population Association of America
1722 N Street N.W.
Washington, D.C. 20036

♦ ♦ ♦ ♦ ♦

Sum It Up

Populations in ecosystems change constantly due to birth, death, or migration. When the biotic and abiotic factors in an ecosystem provide the best possible conditions for growth, a population will increase to its biotic potential. Ecosystems almost never provide ideal conditions for any organisms. Limiting factors, including disease, natural disasters, predators, and limited resources, affect the rate of change in a population.

Using Vocabulary

carrying capacity
limiting factors
population
population density

You are a demographer who has been sent to study the rat population explosion in West Middleton, Anystate, the United States. It seems that the rat population in this small town has doubled within the last two years. You may have to invent some details, but use the four vocabulary words from this lesson to explain what has happened in West Middleton. Plan a solution to the problem. Be sure the vocabulary words and their definitions are clear to someone who has not read this lesson. Check for sense and spelling.

Critical Thinking

1. What has kept the human population small throughout most of human history? Has this changed? Why?
2. What factors might become limiting factors in a country when the population becomes too large?
3. How would limiting factors relate to the density of animal and plant populations?
4. Why has the human population grown in some countries even though the birth rate has decreased?
5. Why do organisms rarely, if ever, reach their biotic potential?

How Do

Populations Interact?

ENERGY! EVERY LIVING THING NEEDS ENERGY,
AND LIFE AS WE KNOW IT COULD NOT EXIST WITHOUT IT.
LET'S FOLLOW THE INTERACTION OF POPULATIONS AND THE TRANSFER
OF ENERGY WITHIN VARIOUS ECOSYSTEMS.

◆　◆　◆　◆　◆

On a typical day, you expend a lot of energy doing many things. Rushing to school, studying mathematics, sharpening a pencil, playing soccer, sitting to watch television, and even growing takes energy. If you were an automobile, your energy would come from burning fossil fuel. If you were a light bulb, you would convert electrical energy to light. Where does the energy that living things use come from?

The photograph on these pages shows an ecosystem that provides energy for all the needs of its living parts. What are the living parts? What is the original energy source that fuels the living parts? In this lesson you will learn how energy flows through the ecosystem.

Minds On! In your *Activity Log* on page 22, draw or list the biotic and abiotic factors in your environment that you use for energy. Are there any living things in your environment that depend on you for energy? (Hint: Think about getting a cold or a sore throat.) In the next Explore Activity, you will examine the food source of one organism.●

Sunlight provides the energy that flows through an ecosystem. Can you trace the flow of energy in this ecosystem?

Activity!

What Does an Owl Eat?

Owls swallow their food whole. The soft parts dissolve in the owl's stomach, and the indigestible parts are regurgitated in the form of a pellet. You can use these remains to determine the relationship of barn owls to their environment.

What You Need

owl pellet
2 forceps
plastic gloves
metric ruler
paper towel
petri dish
Activity Log pages 23–24

Safety!

What To Do

1 *Safety Tip:* Wear plastic gloves to perform this activity . Be careful with sharp objects. Place the owl pellet on the paper towel. Use the forceps to carefully separate the bones of the animals from the hair and fur.

See the *Safety Tip* in step 1.

2 Remove the fur from the bones with the forceps and place the bones in the petri dish. Dispose of the fur as your teacher directs. After you've finished cleaning the bones, wash your hands thoroughly.

3 Sort the bones by shape. Use forceps to put the skull bones in 1/2 of the petri dish.

Shrew

House mouse

Meadow vole

Deer mouse

Mole

Rodent

Rabbit

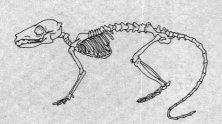
Generalized mammal skeleton

Generalized bird skeleton

4 Match the skulls that you found in the owl pellet with the skulls shown above or with pictures in a field guide.

5 Record the number of skulls of different animals in the data table in your *Activity Log*.

6 On the chalkboard, make a class record of the kinds and numbers of animals found in owl pellets.

7 Dispose of the bones as your teacher directs. Wash your hands thoroughly at the conclusion of the activity.

What Happened?

1. What kinds of materials did you identify in the owl pellet?
2. How many individual vertebrates do you think your collection of bones represents?
3. Did you find any invertebrate material?
4. How many different species of animals do you think the bones represent?

What Now?

1. If the owl that produced your owl pellet regurgitates one pellet each day, how many prey animals does it eat?
2. What is an owl's role in a field environment?
3. What other animals have the same role as an owl in a field environment?

EXPLORE

Interactions Move Energy Through an Ecosystem

In the previous activity, what did you find in the owl pellet? Chances are your owl ate more than one vole or mouse before regurgitating the pellet. Barn owls live in fields where populations of these animals, their food source, also live. A large population of the food source for small mammals lives in the field, too—grasses.

Where does the energy that you, the barn owl, and all other living things need to grow and stay alive come from? In the ecosystem pictured on pages 66 and 67, energy was transferred from the sun to the grass, from the grass to the sheep, and from the sheep to a person. Energy enters an ecosystem in the form of sunlight interacting with and changing organisms and the physical environment. Energy transfers are essential to every organism on Earth.

Green plants use energy from the sun to produce food in the process of photosynthesis. Because they make their own food, green plants are called *producers*. Organisms such as the barn owl, the mouse, and the cow, which don't make their own food but eat other organisms, are called *consumers*. What are you—a producer or consumer?

What type of organisms does the barn owl eat— plants, animals, or both? Because it eats only other animals, the barn owl is known as a *carnivore*. Frogs, snakes, and wolves are all carnivores too. Antwrens, birds found in the tropical rain forest, are also carnivores—they eat insects.

Can you think of any animals that eat only plants? The dairy cow is one such animal. Animals that eat only plants are known as *herbivores*.

You might wonder if you are a carnivore or an herbivore. You are neither, actually. Humans are *omnivores,* organisms that can eat both plants and animals. Other omnivores include bears and raccoons.

Field mouse

Food Chain of the Barn Owl

Barn owl

Grasses

Energy flows through an ecosystem just as water, carbon, and nitrogen do. Energy is transferred through a community as organisms produce food and consume food. Energy flows from producers to consumers as each population eats and is eaten. A **food chain** is a series of organisms that feed on other organisms. In the food chain of the barn owl illustrated on this page, energy flows from the sun to the grass to the mice and from the mice to the owls. When the owls die, they are consumed by small organisms.

71

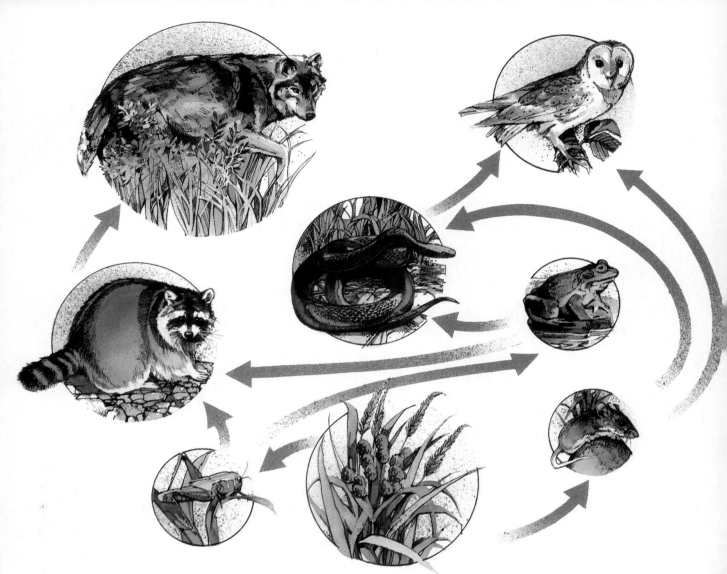

The illustration on this page shows a series of overlapping food chains. A **food web** is a series of interlinking food chains. Use the food web to identify which populations the snake eats and is eaten by. You can see that a food web is more complicated than a food chain. A food chain shows one population that eats or is eaten by another population. A food web shows how one population can be part of more than one food chain.

Revisit the ecosystem you made in the Try This Activity on page 9. Observe and record, in your *Activity Log* page 3, how the organisms in the terrarium relate to each other in a food chain. Illustrate, using words and pictures, how the food chains overlap to form a food web.

Food webs show clearly the interdependence of all biotic factors in an ecosystem. Biotic factors in ecosystems affect each other in many ways. If an organism no

A food web is made up of interlinking food chains. Which are producers? Which are consumers?

longer fills its place in a food web, how will this affect the ecosystem? Do the Try This Activity on the next page to explore this idea.

Activity!

The Domino Effect

Have you ever lined up dominoes in a row and toppled the first one? What happens? All the dominoes fall down. In this activity you will be able to make some inferences about how a change in one population within a food web can have widespread effects on the other populations there.

What You Need

game cards, string, scissors, transparent tape, construction paper, ruler, *Activity Log* page 25

Cut out the cards from the paper your teacher has provided. Cut a strip of construction paper the size of a ruler. Write *sunlight* across it. Arrange the plant cards in a row, and link each one to the sunlight card by laying string to connect them. Now, link an herbivore to each plant card, and a carnivore to each herbivore. You may link two or more cards to a food source, but be sure each animal is linked to its proper food source. Note your final arrangement.

Half the plant population is destroyed by a fire! Remove four plant cards. Rearrange the rest of the web so that all animals have a food source. You can't attach more than two cards to the same food source. If there are extra cards left over, remove them— these populations have died out. In your *Activity Log*, record which organisms besides plants were affected by the fire.

Disasters can affect entire populations and, therefore, the flow of energy through the food chain.

As you saw in the Try This Activity you just did, a change in a food web has effects throughout the ecosystem because it changes the way energy is transferred, or the amount of energy available. Destroying the producers in an ecosystem, as you did in the activity, has a great impact because producers are the organisms that make energy available to the *entire* ecosystem.

Energy pyramid

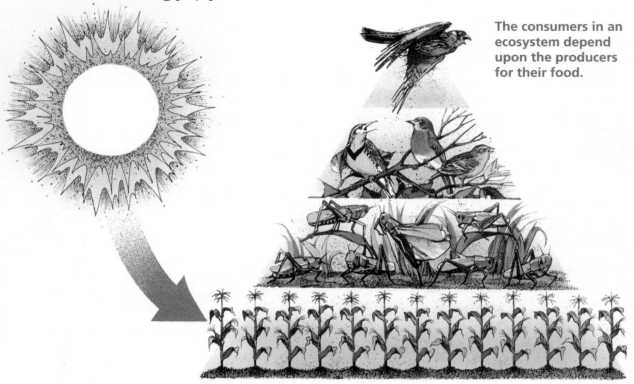

The consumers in an ecosystem depend upon the producers for their food.

Not all of the energy trapped by plants can be used by animals under the best conditions. The diagram on this page is an **energy pyramid,** which shows the amount of energy flowing from one organism to the next through a food chain. As energy moves through an ecosystem, it takes different forms. Producers such as grass or rain forest trees change carbon dioxide and water in the presence of light from the sun into chemical energy during photosynthesis. Energy passes through food chains mainly in the form of chemical energy. The bottom layer of the pyramid shows the amount of energy made available by producers—the base of all energy in the food chain.

Herbivores, such as grasshoppers, eat producers, such as corn. As energy is passed from one organism to another, say from corn to grasshoppers, only some of the energy will be converted in the grasshopper. For every 100 calories of corn eaten by grasshoppers, only 10 calories will be passed on to the birds that eat grasshoppers. Only one calorie of the energy provided by the original corn will be made available to the animals that eat the birds.

A pyramid is a good way to show the flow of energy through an ecosystem because the pyramid gets narrower as it goes up. How many organisms are pictured at the top of the energy pyramid shown? What happens to the number of organisms shown in the energy pyramid as you move up the pyramid from the base to the top? Since the energy available from food decreases at each higher level of the pyramid, an organism in the pyramid is depending on all the organisms below it for energy. As you go up the pyramid, it takes more and more organisms to provide enough energy for life.

What Is a Population's Place in an Ecosystem?

A **community** consists of all the populations that live together in an area. If you say that barn owls live in a field community, you're including information about the populations with which the barn owls live. If you say that barn owls live in barns or fields, you're identifying the owls' habitat. **Habitat** is the place where a population lives. Other populations could share the barn owls' habitat—perhaps barn swallows live in the barn, or hawks live in the same field where the owls live. Obviously, the mice and voles live in the owls' habitat, too. An ecosystem has many habitats within it, with many populations occupying each

habitat. The ecosystem of the barn owl might include a barn, a field, a pond, a stream, and a small clump of trees.

Each population has a particular role, or function, in its habitat, much as you have a particular role in your household. The role or function of an organism in a community is its **niche.** Although many populations share a habitat, only one population can occupy a niche. While the barn owl shares the barn with swallows, the barn owl's niche is the eating of small mammals in the field; the swallow's niche is the eating of insects.

In the tropical rain forest, a community might consist of

insects, trees, monkeys, several different populations of antwrens, and bear-like patos (pa toz′), among many other organisms. Each species of antwrens has a different habitat since each species inhabits a different level of the forest, feeding on the insects living there. If all the antwren species lived on the same level and ate insects, they'd be occupying the same niche. The monkeys and patos live in the same habitat—the canopy layer. They also have the same niche—they feed on fruit. However, they manage to share this niche because patos feed at night and monkeys feed during the day.

Interactions Among Populations

Earlier you studied the owl pellet and determined which field community populations the owl interacts with in a very important way— which ones it eats or gets energy from. You looked at its place in the food chain—the barn owl eats small mammals such as field mice. When one organism hunts and eats another, this interaction is called **predation.** In its relationship with field mice, the barn owl is a predator. The field mice are prey.

Antwrens prey on insects within the tropical rain forest community.

Rufous-rumped antwren, ▶ canopy layer.
Rufous-tailed antwren, shrub and lower understory ▼

▲ **Plain-throated antwren, shrub and herb layer**

FOCUS ON ENVIRONMENT

Operation Owl Prowl

Humans have used predator/prey relationships to benefit both themselves and the predator. Naturalists in some cities have brought in peregrine (per′ ə grin) falcons to kill out-of-control pigeon populations, a potential health hazard. Gardeners place ladybugs and praying mantises in their gardens to eliminate harmful insects. Controlling pests by bringing in a predator can eliminate or reduce our need for poisons to kill the pests. Because all parts of an ecosystem interact, introducing a poison into an environment can harm not only the pest but also other organisms.

In 1990 the New York City Parks Department launched Operation Owl Prowl to determine whether barn owls could be used to kill city rats. Rats pose a health hazard for humans because they carry serious diseases. Rats are sometimes responsible for contaminating human food sources with *Salmonella,* a bacteria that causes a type of food poisoning. Rats also sometimes transmit a virus to humans when they bite them, causing another flu-like disease. For years the parks department had relied exclusively on poison to kill off the rat population and control these diseases. But rat poison has caused as many problems as it has solved.

To find out whether barn owls would eat city rats, parks department naturalists did just what you did in the Explore Activity on pages 68 and 69—they examined hundreds of owl pellets collected from open meadows within city limits where barn owls live. In addition to the bones of house mice and meadow voles, the naturalists found rat bones, rat teeth, rat whiskers, and rat fur in the pellets.

Operation Owl Prowl then moved into a second stage. Park workers built plywood nesting boxes, "owl motels," to lure barn owls into the parks during the owls' nesting season. Each owl family that "checks in" helps decrease the rat population significantly—by as much as 18 rats per night. Unfortunately, since owls don't hunt outside the parks, and rats live inside as well as outside the parks, the owls alone aren't expected to solve the rat problem in New York City. However, Operation Owl Prowl has reduced—but not eliminated—the use of rat poison in one environment.

A major limiting factor in population growth is the amount of food available. The key to controlling the rat population in city parks is controlling the food supply. What role can you and other humans play in limiting the population growth of rats? By reducing the amount of food thrown away and emptying garbage cans every day, humans could make life very difficult for the city's rats.

New York City Parks Department uses the predator/prey relationship between owls and rats to reduce rat populations.

Vultures have a specific niche within their community.

Whether an organism is a producer or a predator partially determines its niche in the community. The niche of a cattail is to grow at the edge of a pond and produce food. The niche of a mosquito is to suck blood from warm-blooded animals. Do the Try This Activity below to observe a niche you may not have thought about before.

Activity!

What Eats Decaying Matter?

Plants produce food that animals eat. Sometimes animals are killed by another animal. Some animals die from natural causes or from human activity. There is another kind of consumer that lives off dead plant or animal material. You can observe some of the organisms that fill this niche in your environment.

What You Need

plastic cup
12-cm-square piece of plywood
4 small rocks
small piece of raw meat
Activity Log **page 26**

Find a place near a rock, tree, or shrub that won't be disturbed. Bury the plastic cup vertically in the soil as shown. Put the meat in the cup. Then, cover the cup with the plywood. Position

the plywood on the rocks as shown so there's a small space between the plywood and the ground.

Observe the cup twice a day for 2 to 3 days. In your *Activity Log,* record the numbers and types of organisms that you find there. What is the niche of these organisms in the community?

Did you observe many organisms in the previous activity? Some of the organisms living off the meat were *scavengers*. These are a unique group of consumers that feed on dead or dying animals or plants. Perhaps you've seen a flock of vultures swoop down on a dead animal by the roadside to devour it. Scavengers are important in an ecosystem. They help to get rid of dead and decaying material so it doesn't pile up. They begin to break it down so decomposers can act on it.

Decomposers are another group of consumers that break down the remains of dead plants and animals and waste materials into simpler substances. Nitrogen, carbon, and other materials are returned to the soil in the material cycles as dead organisms decompose. Living plants and animals need these materials in order to live. Decomposers such as fungi that grow on rotting logs are parts of the nitrogen cycle, as are microscopic bacteria.

Mutualism is a relationship between two species where both benefit. The seeing-eye dog assists its owner; the owner feeds the dog and provides a safe environment.

You've already explored how populations interact in a community through competition and predation. They also compete for resources such as food and water in a community when they are in limited supply. The population that obtains more resources increases in number over time. The population that doesn't, slowly decreases. You explored the predatory relationships of the barn owl when you examined its pellet. Organisms also interact in another type of relationship within a community.

Commensalism is a relationship between two species where one benefits and the other is neither helped nor harmed. The bromeliad is raised to brighter sunlight by the tree; the tree experiences no harm as it provides a place for the bromeliad to grow.

Symbiosis

Symbiosis is a specific interaction between two species over a long time; it may or may not be beneficial. Symbiosis means "living together." Ecologists talk about three basic kinds of symbiosis—mutualism, commensalism, and parasitism. These relationships are different from a predator/prey relationship. Predators hunt and kill their prey. A parasite doesn't benefit if it kills its host—it loses its available food source.

Parasitism is a relationship between two species where one benefits and the other is harmed. A lamprey benefits as it attaches itself to a fish and feeds off the fish's blood and other body fluids. The fish is harmed by the lamprey, which is a parasite. While the parasite harms its host, killing the host isn't beneficial to the parasite.

Human Population Interactions

The bromeliad and the tree, dogs and owners, and lampreys and their host fish are examples of interactions between populations.

How are human populations different from other organisms? We live in the same ecosystems as other organisms and are part of communities and food webs, but we also create a variety of complex habitats and communities for ourselves—cities, farms, and small villages all over Earth.

Humans have some unique roles in their ecosystems. We keep pets such as cats, dogs, or parakeets. We domesticate other animals, such as horses, cows, and chickens, breeding them for a variety of purposes. What type of relationship does a human have with a riding horse? With beef cattle? What would happen to these animals if humans disappeared?

Minds On! On page 27 of your *Activity Log,* list all the populations of different organisms that make up your home or school community. Consider different species of plants and animals, and think about microorganisms. How do the populations in your community interact? Identify one mutual, commensal, and parasitic relationship found there. Don't forget to include yourself when thinking about these relationships.●

What is the source of energy for each population you included in your community in the Minds On? How can you now use what you know about producers, consumers, food chains, and food webs to describe how energy flows from the sun to other populations in your community? What would happen to the flow of energy if the number of one population somehow changed?

High-rise apartments, Hong Kong

Humans enter into the ecosystem, changing interactions among populations.

Humans create their own habitats. You live in a house, trailer, or apartment that was constructed by someone. Air conditioning, central heating, electric lights, and plumbing change the abiotic factors of our habitats. Your role in this habitat is your niche. If it's your job to take out the garbage, that's part of your niche. As a student, part of your niche is to study and learn.

Humans also change their habitats frequently. How many times have you moved during your life? Have you moved from a different biome or a different country? What effects did moving have on your life? Did your niche change? Do the Language Arts Link on this page to consider the changes in habitat that you've had.

Language Arts Link

Habitat Is Where You Hang Your Hat

Habitat is the place where a population lives. Your habitat may be centered around your address. Write an essay in your *Activity Log* on page 28 about a time when you lived in a different habitat from the one you live in now, such as when you vacationed at camp or lived in another house (perhaps in another state or country). Compare and contrast that habitat and the one you live in now, noting the differences and similarities.

Freezing is a natural disaster that can destroy entire populations such as orange trees.

All organisms depend upon each other for this cycling of energy within an ecosystem. When humans change habitats, energy requirements within an ecosystem do not change, but energy sources may. If a natural disaster, such as freezing temperatures, damages orange trees in Florida, then there is a limited amount of fresh oranges available to humans. If large numbers of cattle or chickens are dying from disease, injury, or environmental causes, then production of beef, milk, poultry, and eggs is limited.

A natural, undisturbed ecosystem remains fairly stable within the normal pattern of succession. However, the action of humans can have a drastic effect on plant and animal populations within an ecosystem. The devastating effects of human-induced forest fires can wipe out thousands of ecological communities within minutes. Remember, each organism within an ecosystem, other than primary producers, is dependent upon other organisms for its source of energy.

A growing area of science is that of applied ecology. Its purpose is to educate humans on the importance of preserving and managing our natural resources in an effort to protect the environment with the understanding that maintaining our natural ecosystems is beneficial to society. Learning about ecology and focusing on the environment can help us appreciate the role each of us plays in this energy cycle of life. Reading the following Literature Link can help you appreciate even the interaction we have with *Small Worlds* within an ecosystem.

Literature  Link

🐜 *Small Worlds*

Life exists everywhere around you, whether you live in an old house downtown in a city, or along a sleepy country lane. You can observe communities and their interactions wherever you are. The book *Small Worlds* by Howard E. Smith, Jr. describes many unusual ecosystems that you can find around you. Pick one and explore it, using the book as a guide. Observe your ecosystem for at least a week.

Write a report on your observations, including the biotic and abiotic factors you see, the populations you observe, and any interactions you observe. What does each population eat? Do you see any examples of competition, predation, or symbiosis? Did you see any changes over time? Finally, include your role in this ecosystem.

◆   ◆   ◆   ◆   ◆

Sum It Up

All living parts of an ecosystem need energy for growth and development. Energy flows through an ecosystem by the interactions of the populations that make up its community in a food chain and within a larger food web. Producers are responsible for converting sunlight into chemical energy that can be used by consumers. Animals acquire energy by consuming plants or other animals in predatory or parasitic relationships. The way an organism provides or consumes energy in its habitat is its niche, or part, in the ecosystem. Since the energy used at each link of a food chain is not transferred completely to the next link, organisms higher up on an energy pyramid depend on all the organisms below them for their energy intake. Since all the organisms are dependent on each other for the flow of energy, a change in the ecosystem affects all parts of it.

Using Vocabulary

| community | food chain | habitat | predation |
| energy pyramid | food web | niche | symbiosis |

Pick an animal. Develop the food chain for that animal. You may need to use an encyclopedia to check your facts. Tie the animal and its food chain into a larger food web. List the first animal's niche, habitat, and community. Is this animal a predator or does it have some other relationship to the animals in its community? Take the information you have gathered and illustrate the food chain and web, including the important facts and vocabulary words.

Critical Thinking

1. What is the difference between a community and a population?
2. Why do two species usually not occupy the same niche?
3. Which of the following groups are necessary for life on Earth—producers, consumers, decomposers? Why?
4. Which of these food chains will support more people? Why? Corn consumed by humans? Corn consumed by cow—cow consumed by humans?
5. What would happen to the food chains in an area if all the plants were to die?

How Does an Ecosystem Change?

HOW DOES AN ECOSYSTEM FORM? HOW DOES IT CHANGE OVER TIME? WHAT HAPPENS IF THE ENVIRONMENT IS DISTURBED?

◆　◆　◆　◆　◆

Suppose you had a birthday party when you were three years old. Your parents took photographs of you and your guests eating cake and ice cream and playing games. Some of the people who are still in your class today attended the party. If you showed them the photos, would they recognize themselves?

You and your friends have changed quite a lot since you were three. Even though your appearance and what you know has changed, you're still the same person you were at three. People who've known you all your life could describe things about you, such as the way you smile or the texture of your hair, that have stayed the same. The person you have become has evolved from the person you were. Like people, ecosystems change in some predictable ways over time.

Minds On! Look at the picture on this page. As you may be able to tell from the barn, this land was once a farm. The photograph reflects some changes that occurred after the woman who owned this farm, Emily Freytag, left her farm to take a city job. What happened after the owner left the farm and moved to the city?

Think about how this farmland might have looked five years ago. What kinds of plants and animals lived there then? Write an answer in your *Activity Log* on page 29. Then, predict what you think the land will look like in five years.●

Farmlands change, and so do other ecosystems. In the next Explore Activity, you will discover the changing variety of populations in a freshwater ecosystem.

The now-abandoned Freytag farm was on a deciduous forest.

Activity!

How Does Pond Water Change?

In the previous Minds On, you pictured what changes would happen to an abandoned farm within the next five years. Change takes place in water ecosystems as well as on land such as the Freytags' farm. In this activity you will observe what happens in pond water over time and draw conclusions about what you observe.

What You Need

1 tall jar/lid
dried pond vegetation
distilled water
pH paper
microscope
microscope slides
coverslips
droppers
***Activity Log* pages 30–31**

What To Do

1 Place some dried plants from a pond into a clean jar. Fill the jar with distilled water. Test the acidity of the water with pH paper, and record whether the water is acidic or basic in your ***Activity Log***. Place the lid on the jar.

2 Place the jar in a place that has light and a constant temperature of at least 21°C (70°F).

3 Observe the jar each day for 5 to 10 days. If any water evaporates, add some distilled water to refill it to the original level. Note the color, cloudiness, odor, and any layers that might be settling out. Record the date and your observations in your ***Activity Log***.

4 On the first day you see changes in the water, test the water with the pH paper and record the results in your ***Activity Log***.

  See *Safety Tip* in step 5.

5 Take a sample of water from the top of the jar using the dropper. Drop 1 to 2 drops of pond water on a slide. *Safety Tip:* Be careful with glass slides and coverslips. Place the coverslip on the slide as your teacher has demonstrated. Examine the slide under the microscope, first on low power, and then on high power. Make sketches in your **Activity Log** of any organisms you see.

6 Repeat step 5, taking a sample of water from the middle of the jar, and then the bottom, using a clean dropper each time.

7 Repeat steps 4, 5, and 6 every 2 days for the remainder of the 5- to 10-day observation period.

What Happened?

1. How many different kinds of organisms did you observe the first time you observed the water?
2. Did you observe any changes in the types of organisms from the first appearance and the end of the activity?
3. Where did the organisms come from?

What Now?

1. How can you explain the changes you saw?
2. Would you expect other samples of pond water to be the same? Why or why not?

How Do Ecosystems Change?

In the Explore Activity on pages 86 and 87, you observed a community in a jar of water as it changed over ten days. The water you put in the jar had nothing living in it. However, the pond vegetation carried some organisms into the jar. The first populations you observed were various microorganisms, probably *protists* with flagella or cilia. After several days, a green scum of algae may have formed on top of the water or on the sides of the glass. Then you probably observed simple animals such as *rotifers*. The same changes occur as a freshwater ecosystem forms, perhaps when a reservoir is created or an unused quarry is allowed to fill with rainwater. Fish, amphibians, complex plants, and animals that feed on these organisms might eventually become a part of the freshwater ecosystem.

Think about the patterns of change you observed. There were more populations in the community after five days than after three days, and still more after ten days. After day nine, did your pond community have large numbers of the organisms that you noted in the early days of the activity? Populations in communities also change in

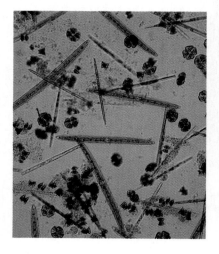

Protists, both plant and animal, were the first organisms to appear in the water.

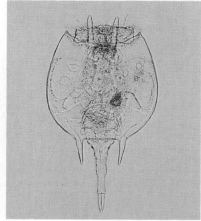

Rotifers are simple animals that feed on protists.

size as an ecosystem is forming. As the populations of more complex organisms, such as rotifers, increased in the jar of pond water, the populations of one-celled organisms decreased. The organisms that appeared first were eaten by those that appeared last. Later populations depended on the first ones.

Populations in a community sometimes completely replace each other over time. Wild grass, shrubs, and field mice replaced corn, soybeans, and pigs on the abandoned farm you saw on pages 84 and 85. When beavers dam a stream to form a pond, grass and shrubs on the stream bank are replaced with frogs and

algae. The process by which plant and animal populations are replaced over time by different plant and animal populations is called **succession** (sǝk sesh′ ǝn).

Why does succession happen? The climate, soil, and nutrients available in an area determine the types of organisms that can survive there. If *one* of these factors changes, the community will change. If an area of tropical rain forest biome suddenly became dry for some reason, most of the plants would die because they are adapted to a wet climate. Animals that depended on the plants for food would die or migrate. The abandoned farm changed because

Natural occurrences such as the eruption of Mount St. Helens can destroy the biotic factors in an ecosystem.

Starting With Nothing

The community in the abandoned field shown on pages 84 and 85 changed after the farmer stopped planting crops on it. However, in the Explore Activity on pages 86 and 87, a community formed where none had existed before. Nothing lived in the distilled water in the jar before you added the vegetation. The process of succession occurred in both cases, but they are different types of succession.

The picture on this page shows the 1980 eruption of Mount St. Helens, which was mentioned in Lesson 2. Volcanic eruptions and other natural events such as earthquakes, floods, fires, and droughts can destroy the biotic factors in an ecosystem. Human activities such as the formation of reservoirs or strip mining can also destroy entire communities. If a community is destroyed and there is no further disturbance, another community will slowly replace the one that was destroyed.

Succession of the type that occurred on Mount St. Helens and in the jar of sterile pond water is called primary succession. **Primary succession** is the formation of a community in an area where no previous organisms existed and involves the formation of soil. This type of succession usually takes centuries to occur.

the farmer was no longer there to plant, water, and fertilize the corn and soybean crops. The wild grass could survive in the field without the farmer, but the corn couldn't. As a pond formed in a field, grass could not survive in the water, but algae could. The process of succession continues until the abiotic factors stabilize and the populations that make up the community are adapted to these conditions and to each other.

Lichens are the first organisms to grow after violent destruction of the biotic factors in an ecosystem.

During the eruption of Mount St. Helens, molten rock and volcanic ash covered the ground around the volcano. When the molten rock cooled, the eruption area was covered in barren volcanic rock and ash. Nothing lived on the rock or in the thick layer of ash at this time. Soon, however, spores and bits of dust or dirt carrying microorganisms were carried by wind or rain onto the rock. Seeds of small plants were carried into the ash where some could germinate. An ecosystem began to form.

The first organism to grow in an area is a **pioneer species.** Photosynthetic bacteria, algae, or lichens (lī′ kənz) are usually the pioneer species in primary succession because they can produce their own food and survive harsh conditions. Lichens are especially important in primary succession. Lichens consist of fungus and cyanobacteria living in a symbiotic relationship. The cyanobacteria provide food for the fungus, and the fungus attaches the lichen to the rock. Chemicals the fungus excretes, temperature changes, wind, rain, and ice cause the volcanic rock to break. When these abiotic factors break down the rocks on Earth's surface into mineral particles, soil begins to form.

Dead lichens, algae, or bacteria add humus to the mineral particles. As the new soil builds, plants begin to grow in it, and their roots break the rock even further. Animals will migrate into the

Populations in a community, such as this freshwater pond, sometimes completely replace each other.

Changes in our environment often reflect secondary succession.

area to eat the plants. As these plants and animals die and decompose, they add more nutrients to the soil. The changes will progress until a stable community develops.

After a Disturbance

What happens to an existing ecosystem that is disturbed? **Secondary succession** is the process that occurs when an existing community is disturbed and the area gradually returns to its previous condition. Human activities such as logging and ranching can change ecosystems and begin the process of secondary succession. When people log in a tropical rain forest, the ecosystem is changed—the tree population is decreased, more sunlight and rain reach the forest floor, and the habitat and food supply of many organisms are destroyed. When farmers clear grassland and plant it with crops, the community has changed. Natural disasters such as fires that disturb an existing ecosystem also cause secondary succession to begin. The Try This Activity below will guide you in investigating the process of secondary succession where you live.

TRY THIS

Activity!

Restoration in Process

What happens after an ecosystem is disturbed? What does the process of succession involve? Any area around you that has been disturbed, such as an abandoned lot or house, a demolished building, or a pond that is drying up, will be in the process of secondary succession. In this activity, you will observe restoration in process.

What You Need

field guide to plants in your area (optional)
Activity Log **page 32**

Visit an area near your school or home that has been recently disturbed, preferably within the past month or so. In your *Activity Log,* list changes you see taking place. Also, describe how this area compares to the surrounding community. Using the field guide, identify the major plant species in this disturbed area, list them in your *Activity Log,* and compare this area to the major plants for your biome. Hypothesize what plants and animals will live here in a year, and write a description of what the area will look like in your *Activity Log*.

What did you imagine would happen to the abandoned farm on pages 84 and 85 in five years? After a disturbance an area will slowly return to the community that existed before the disturbance, if there is no further interference. On a farm, the corn won't come up in the summer if it isn't planted in the spring. The farmers are no longer there to plant the corn.

Secondary Succession
From Farmland to Forest

The chart on this page shows the pattern of change in the process of secondary succession in an abandoned farm field. Each community that forms during succession is determined by the community before. The first community to appear after a community has been disrupted is the **pioneer community.**

What happens in the second and third year after the farm is abandoned? How is the first community changing? Why is the pioneer community changing? After the pioneer communities came the tall grasses and plants, and the mice, rabbits, insects, and seed-eating birds. Grass is the dominant species at this stage, providing food and shelter for the animals. **Dominant species** are those that most strongly affect the community. They determine which other species can survive in the community. The dominant species primarily determines the next step in the process of change.

Since plants are the producers in the community, they are often the dominant species, determining what animals can survive there and what the resulting community is like. For example, as trees

The hot, dry fields of grass are perfect environments for pine seeds to sprout. As pine trees thrive and get bigger, grass can no longer grow in the shade they cast.
▼

In the second and third years after the field is abandoned, tall grass and small plants grow among the crabgrass. The crabgrass can't live in the shade of tall grass and begins to die out. Mice, rabbits, insects, and seed-eating birds are common.
▼

During the first year, a community of crabgrass, insects, and mice invade the field where corn is no longer planted.
▼

Thirty to 70 years after the farm field has been abandoned, deciduous forest has replaced the other communities. The seeds of deciduous trees can grow in ▼ **the shade of the forest floor resulting in new deciduous trees to take the place of trees that die. Squirrels and birds live in the trees.**

A pine forest has replaced the field. Since pine seeds need full sun to germinate, the number of new pine seedlings drops, but the seeds of deciduous trees such as maple, hickory, or oak are able to grow in the shade. ▼

invade the field, animals such as squirrels that nest in trees and eat their seeds and birds that nest in trees, become part of the community. Birds that feed or nest in open fields leave for better habitats. Animals that eat grass or small plants also leave to find better food sources.

In approximately 70 years, what was once a farm has been replaced by a hardwood forest. The hardwood forest could stay on the land for many years. Trees and shrubs live in the community. Animals such as deer, rac-

coons, foxes, and owls receive food and shelter from the forest. Birds nest and feed in the forest.

When the same species live in an area such as a hardwood forest for a long period of time, the community is stable. The plants and animals in this community are well-suited to the soil, climate, and nutrients available in this environment. The species depend on each other. The community stays the same as long as environmental conditions remain the same. The stable community formed at the end of succession is a **climax** (klī′ maks) **community.** The biomes you read about in Lesson 2 are climax communities. The organisms that live in those biomes are adapted to live where they do, and as long as the environment doesn't change, they will continue to live there.

Humans Affect Change

Look back at the photograph of the abandoned farm field at the beginning of this lesson on pages 84 and 85. Think about the history of the area where the farm once was. When Emily Freytag's ancestors cleared the land and began to farm it, they changed the ecosystem that was there. The Freytags plowed under a cleared deciduous forest, where many species of plants and animals lived.

Organisms living in the same place become dependent upon each other. When many plant populations lived in the deciduous forest, each was less likely to be destroyed by insects or plant viruses searching for food. The Freytags replaced the variety of plants with a single food crop—corn—on the cleared land. The corn population was the only food source for many insects and microorganisms in the area. The Freytags had to use pesticides to protect the corn from being consumed. Use what you know about food webs to explain the probable effects of the pesticides on the ecosystem.

An abandoned farm often makes humans feel sad. People don't live there anymore. The barn is falling apart. The land is overrun with brush and weeds. But the process of succession is changing the land now that the farm is gone. You know what the end result of these changes will be —a hardwood forest. Think about how plants such as hardwood trees and animals such as humans interact in the carbon cycle. Emily Freytag lost a farm when she abandoned the land, but she and other people living in the area of the farm gained an important ecosystem.

Emily Freytag didn't make a conscious decision to let the natural process of succession take over on her farm. She moved off the farm for another reason—to take a job in the city. Sometimes, people deliberately abandon land to the process of succession. Sometimes people even try to speed up the process of succession. For example, turning depleted strip mines into terraced forests allows the land to return to the process of succession.

The pictures on these pages show the effects of strip-mining, a process that involves removing topsoil and plants from the surface of Earth to obtain coal that is buried below. Although strip-mining is the cheapest way to remove coal, it scars the landscape and disrupts wildlife habitats. Very few organisms can survive the effects of strip-mining. The good news is that land used for strip-mining can be reclaimed. Reclamation is replacing the topsoil and reseeding with grass and sometimes trees. This does not entirely restore the ecosystem to its original state, but it is a step in the right direction.

In 1977 a law was passed that requires strip-mine operators to prove they can reclaim the land. The area shown in the second picture once looked like the area shown in the first, but the strip-mined land has been reclaimed. Some conservationists believe that more should be done to preserve the ecosystem and that state and federal governments should be more involved in regulating strip-mining and reclamation. In the next Minds On, you will weigh both sides of the strip-mining question.

Minds On! You are a government official in the state of West Virginia where many people are employed in the coal-mining industry. Taxpayers have complained about pollution from strip mines and how unattractive they are. Part of your job is to decide how to spend limited tax dollars. In your *Activity Log* on page 33, list the pros and cons of turning the strip mine into reforested land over reclaimed land.●

The Raging Forest Fire Debate

Humans must make many decisions about altering the natural processes that cause ecosystems to evolve. Today, humans also play a role in succession caused by one natural disaster, the forest fire.

Foresters encourage Americans to prevent forest fires. In the case of crown fires, extremely hot fires that destroy all the plants and animals in their wake, prevention is the best course. Crown fires often occur in forests littered with dead wood and ground debris. Ironically, crown fires occur most often where all fire has been prevented for a long time. If a fire does start, all this accumulated "firewood" bursts into a devastating crown fire.

Ground fires are much smaller fires that actually benefit some plants and animals in a forest. These fires burn at low levels in a forest preventing the accumulation of too much dead tree litter that could result in crown fires. Ground fires benefit jack pine and giant sequoia (si kwoi′ ə) trees. The cones of these two trees release their seeds only when they are exposed to the intense heat of a fire. Ground fires are small enough for wildlife to escape them.

Foresters frequently allow ground fires to burn as long as they don't threaten humans. Often when ground fires happen in national parks, tourists complain that the smoke ruins their views—and their vacations. Some people don't want to lose any area of our national forests to fires.

Minds On! Imagine that you are the chief administrator of our national forests. Write a one-page statement on forest fires. Decide whether forest rangers should set ground fires as needed, whether naturally occurring ground fires should be allowed to burn, whether to extinguish all ground fires immediately, or if some combination of these approaches would be most effective.●

The question of controlling forest fires in national and state parks often requires balancing human issues with a knowledge of natural succession.

◆　◆　◆　◆　◆

Sum It Up

When new ecosystems form or an existing ecosystem is disturbed, the process of succession gradually changes the biotic factors over a long period of time, until a stable climax community is reached. Climax communities are areas of biomes where the biotic and abiotic factors interact to maintain a stable environment. Ecosystems first form during the process of primary succession when a pioneer species begins the process of soil formation on an area of new rock. Disturbances such as human activities and natural disasters begin the process of secondary succession. Secondary succession returns the community to its original state, the one best adapted to the environment. The community that forms at each stage of succession is determined by the previous community. As human development intrudes into ecosystems and disturbs the natural processes of succession, an understanding of succession and climax communities can prevent human-made ecological disasters.

Using Vocabulary

climax community　　**pioneer community**　　**secondary succession**
dominant species　　　**pioneer species**　　　**succession**
　　　　　　　　　　　　primary succession

You are an ecologist hired by the government of Brazil. You have been asked to develop a plan to encourage the succession of an area that was previously slashed and burned to a tropical rain forest climax community. Using the vocabulary words listed above, describe your plan. Might you "seed" the area with plants or animals? Which kinds might you use? Check the definitions of the terms to be sure you use them correctly. You may either present your plan orally or as a written report.

Critical Thinking

1. What might be a possible climax community of an abandoned farm?
2. How would succession be affected if animals did not return to an area after a fire?
3. Climax communities are different in different parts of the country. What abiotic factors might affect the kinds of climax communities that will develop in a given area?
4. What conditions cause secondary succession to occur?
5. How are primary succession and secondary succession different?

We're All in This Together

◆　◆　◆　◆　◆

Ecosystems on Earth, including the one you live in, consist of living and nonliving parts that interact in various ways to shape the steady state composition of the ecosystem and determine whether and how it changes.

In Lesson 1 you imagined yourself as part of an island ecosystem. Think about how much more information you can get now from the island photograph than when you first considered what you would need to survive on an island. Like an ecologist, you can use the kinds of plants growing on the island and the animals that live there as clues to the humidity, temperature, and the type of food and water available. You can observe the interactions that cause energy to flow through food chains and food webs, and determine what place in an energy pyramid you and your family would occupy. You can gauge the amount of light that reaches the ground by observing the height and density of the trees.

Suppose once again that you are stranded on the island. How many trees should you cut down to build a cabin? Fifteen would make a nice clearing. However, you know how cutting down the trees will affect the shade plants that grow underneath them and the animals whose habitat is in the trees. You decide not to take more than you need—four trees will be enough.

Now that you know more about ecosystems, would you do anything differently?

You want to plant a garden to cultivate some wild plants you have found. It would be easiest to burn down a section of trees. That will destroy some habitat for tree-dwelling animals and possibly a food source for some animals. And what will happen in a few years when the nutrients in the soil have been used up? What if you have to burn more and more forest? How fast will it regrow? You decide to clear only a small patch near the edge of a forest, and to leave some small trees around it. You make a compost of your food scraps and dead vegetation. This will provide fertilizer so your soil does not wear out as quickly. You also decide to put dead leaves around the plants as mulch to keep the soil from eroding. You are going to change the land as little as possible and return nutrients to the soil so it will last as long as possible.

Being stranded on an island would make a lot of people anxious. Perhaps when you first land on the island, you're so afraid of running out of food that you catch more fish and pick more tropical fruit than you can possibly eat. Then you remember that everything you do to an ecosystem has an effect on all parts of it. You set down the fishing pole you made from a tree branch and remind yourself that you don't want to decrease the fish population too much, or there won't be enough fish to feed the sea birds and mammals. You pick only the fruit you need at the moment. You want to leave some fruit on the trees to provide food for the birds and animals and to sprout into new plants.

You have learned more about biotic and abiotic factors and their interaction in the ecosystem. In the unit introduction, you created a terrarium, an enclosed environment, and were asked to observe it as you studied this unit. Do the Try This Activity on the next page and catch up on your ecosystem.

Mexico's Tarascon Indians fish in a way that encourages careful use of resources.

A conservatory like the one at Longwood Gardens, Pennsylvania, is simply a large terrarium. What things might it have in common with the terrarium you created at the beginning of this Unit?

Activity!

An Ecosystem Revisited

As you progressed through the lessons, were you observing the interactions and changes in the terrarium you made at the beginning of the unit? What parts and interactions that you have studied did you observe in this simple enclosed ecosystem?

What You Need

terrarium from Try This Activity page 9
Activity Log page 34

Use your observations from the past weeks to discuss and answer the following questions. Record your answers in your *Activity Log*. List the abiotic and biotic factors you observed. Which cycles did you observe? List the parts of the ecosystem that worked together in these cycles. Did any of the populations in your ecosystem change? How did the populations interact? What was the food chain? Explain the changes that you observed over time. When you're finished, prepare a report from your group, including diagrams to illustrate your points when possible. Assign each member of the group a different piece of the report to prepare. One diagram should show the flow of energy through your ecosystem.

While it is helpful to observe a terrarium to make some generalizations about ecosystems, a terrarium is a closed ecosystem—one without human interaction. Where you live, you will find humans to be part of the ecosystem. What people do affects all parts of the ecosystem. Do the next Try This Activity to apply these concepts to another ecosystem.

Toads are one of the most common amphibians in the deciduous forest biome.

Activity!

Amphibitat

You know that biotic and abiotic factors make up an ecosystem and that each part of an ecosystem is dependent upon the other parts. Ecologists have noted a recent decline in the amphibian population worldwide. Scientists have been observing and collecting data on the population decrease hoping to discover why the population is declining. While fewer amphibians in the world may not seem like a big issue at first glance, the interdependence of organisms within the ecosystem tells the ecologists that something is wrong. Try on the hat of an ecologist in this activity to see if you understand Earth's ecosystems.

What You Need
optional—crayons, markers, or colored pencils
Activity Log page 35

You are part of a group of individuals chosen to study the the reduction in amphibian populations recently seen worldwide. You are creating an enclosed, controlled environment that will include some larger animals as well as smaller ones. Those included are part of the deciduous forest biome. Your goal is to determine the best conditions for amphibian growth.

Use drawings, words, or both in your *Activity Log*. If you wish, use pictures out of old magazines to illustrate Amphibitat (Amphibian Habitat), or make a model. If you're working in a group, plan Amphibitat together and assign different parts of the description to individuals. Consider the following questions when you design your ecosystem. Where will the energy for your energy pyramid come from? What abiotic factors do amphibians need to live? Are they compatible with those abiotic factors humans need? What conditions would produce optimum population growth? What limiting factors will affect amphibian population growth? Would including predators to the amphibians be helpful or harmful? Will your mission to observe amphibians in a protected environment be successful? Can you project what the future might hold? When you're finished, share your Amphibitat with your class.

What might the drop in
numbers of amphibians tell
ecologists about Earth's
ecosystems?

GLOSSARY

Use the pronunciation key below to help you decode, or read, the pronunciations.

Pronunciation Key

a	at, bad	d	dear, soda, bad
ā	ape, pain, day, break	f	five, defend, leaf, off, cough, elephant
ä	father, car, heart	g	game, ago, fog, egg
âr	care, pair, bear, their, where	h	hat, ahead
e	end, pet, said, heaven, friend	hw	white, whether, which
ē	equal, me, feet, team, piece, key	j	joke, enjoy, gem, page, edge
i	it, big, English, hymn	k	kite, bakery, seek, tack, cat
ī	ice, fine, lie, my	l	lid, sailor, feel, ball, allow
îr	ear, deer, here, pierce	m	man, family, dream
o	odd, hot, watch	n	not, final, pan, knife
ō	old, oat, toe, low	ng	long, singer, pink
ô	coffee, all, taught, law, fought	p	pail, repair, soap, happy
ôr	order, fork, horse, story, pour	r	ride, parent, wear, more, marry
oi	oil, toy	s	sit, aside, pets, cent, pass
ou	out, now	sh	shoe, washer, fish mission, nation
u	up, mud, love, double	t	tag, pretend, fat, button, dressed
ū	use, mule, cue, feud, few	th	thin, panther, both
ü	rule, true, food	th	this, mother, smooth
ů	put, wood, should	v	very, favor, wave
ûr	burn, hurry, term, bird, word, courage	w	wet, weather, reward
ə	about, taken, pencil, lemon, circus	y	yes, onion
b	bat, above, job	z	zoo, lazy, jazz, rose, dogs, houses
ch	chin, such, match	zh	vision, treasure, seizure

abiotic factors (ā′ bī ot′ ik) the nonliving parts of an ecosystem such as soil and light

aquaculture (ak′ wa kul′ chər) the raising of aquatic animals and plants, such as shellfish or seaweed, for food; underwater agriculture

biome (bī′ ōm) a complex community of plants and animals living in a particular geographical area with a particular climate

biotic factors (bī ot′ ik) the living parts of an ecosystem such as plants and animals

biotic potential (bī ot′ ik pə ten′ shəl) the number of organisms that could be produced under the best possible conditions

canopy (kan′ ə pē) the layer of the tropical rain forest 30–40 meters above the ground. Trees are so closely intertwined that there is little space between them

carnivore (kär′ nə vôr′) an animal or plant with a diet primarily of meat

carrying capacity (kâr′ ē ing′ kə pas′ i tē) the number of individuals of a population that an environment can support

cilia (sil′ ē ə) similar hairlike structures on certain cells, such as paramecia, that move to and fro allowing the cell to move

climate (klī′ mit) the typical weather conditions of a particular place or region, usually considered in terms of average temperature, humidity, rainfall, and wind conditions.

climax (klī′ maks) **community** the final stage in the ecological development of a given community of plants, animals, and other organisms, in which species are stable and perpetuate themselves as long as the same ecological conditions persist

commensalism (kə men′ sə liz′ əm) a relationship between two organisms of different kinds in which one is benefitted and the other is neither benefitted nor harmed

community (kə mū′ ni tē) all the animals, plants, and other organisms that live in a certain area and interact with each other, considered as a group

consumers (kən sü′ mərz) organisms, usually animals, that feed on another organisms

crown fire (kroun fīr) an extremely hot, rapidly burning forest fire that destroys all organisms in its wake; commonly occurs in forests that have not had recent ground fires

deciduous forest (di sij′ ü əs) a forest primarily of trees that lose their leaves seasonally

decomposer (dē′ kəm pō′ zər) an organism, such as a bacterium, that breaks down dead plant and animal matter into simpler substances that can be used by other organisms

desert (dez′ ərt) a sandy or rocky region with very little rainfall, having little or no vegetation

dominant species (dom ə nənt spē′ shēz) those species that most strongly affect the community

ecology (ē kol′ ə jē) a branch of biology that deals with the relationships of living things to their surroundings and to each other

ecosystem (ek′ ō sis′ təm, ē′ kō sis′ təm) all the living and nonliving things within a particular area and their relationship to each other and to their physical environment

emergent layer (i mûr′ jənt) trees in the tropical rain forest that stand 10 to 20 meters above the canopy layer

energy pyramid (en′ ər jē pîr′ ə mid′) a diagram that shows the flow of energy through a food chain with producers at the base and consumers in the upper levels

environmentalist (en vī′ rən men′ tə list) a person who is concerned about the quality of the environment, especially about the effects of pollution of Earth's air, land, and water and the exhaustion of Earth's air, land, and water and the exhaustion of Earth's natural resources

estuary (es′ chü er′ ē) the place where a body of fresh water meets the ocean

flagella (flə jel′ ə) long whiplike tails or parts that enable certain cells, bacteria, and protozoa to move

food chain (füd chān′) a sequence of the living things of a community, in which each plant, animal, or other organism in the sequence feeds upon the one below it

food web (füd web) a network of interrelated food chains in an ecological community

grassland (gras′ land′) an area of irregular rainfall where varieties of grasses are the primary plants

habitat (hab′ i tat′) that area or region in which an animal or plant naturally lives or grows

herbivore (hûr′ bə vôr′) any animal that feeds chiefly on plants

latitude (lat′ i tüd′) the distance north or south of the equator, measured in a unit called a degree

limiting factor (lim′ it ing′ fak′ tər) a condition in the environment that stops a population from increasing in size

mutualism (mū′ chü ə liz′ əm) a symbiotic relationship between two different kinds of organisms that benefits both of them

niche (nich) status or role of an organism within its community

omnivore (om′ nə vôr′) an organism that eats both plants and animals

parasitism (par′ ə sit′ izm) relationship in which one organism lives on and may harm another organism called a host

pioneer community (pī′ ə nîr′ kə mū′ ni tē) the first community to appear after a community has been disrupted

pioneer species (pī′ ə nîr′ spē′ shēz) the first organism to grow in an area

population (pop′ yə lā shən) all the organisms of one species in a community

population density (pop′ yə lā′ shən den′ si tē) the number of individuals per unit of living space in an environment

predation (pre dā′ shən) when one organism hunts and eats another

primary succession (prī′ mer ē) the formation of a community in an area where no previous organisms existed and involves the formation of soil

producers (prə dü′ sər, prə dū′ sər) organisms, such as plants, that use inorganic substances to make food

protist (prō′ tist) a one-celled organism with both plant-like and animal-like characteristics

regurgitate (rē gûr′ ji tāt′) to rush, pour, or flow back, as liquids, gases, or undigested food

rotifer (rō′ tə fər) any of a large group of many-celled microscopic animals found in ponds and puddles, having a ring of cilia at one end that is used for locomotion and feeding

scavenger (skav′ ən jər) an animal, such as a vulture or hyena, that feeds on decaying plant or animal matter

secondary succession (sək′ ən der′ ē sək sesh ən) the process that occurs when an existing community is disturbed

succession (sək sesh′ ən) process of gradual change in a community in which different species become dominant

symbiosis (sim′ bī ō′ sis, sim′ bē ō′ sēz) the close association of two living things that are not alike

taiga (tī′ gə) any of the northernmost forests of cone-bearing trees in North America, Europe, and Asia

terrarium (tə râr′ ē əm) a small enclosure or container, often of glass, used for growing plants or raising small land animals, such as snakes, turtles, or lizards

tropical rain forest (trop′ i kəl rān fôr′ ist) a hot, humid forest found in low-laying areas near the equator

tundra (tun′ drə) a vast, treeless plain in the northernmost parts of Asia, Europe, and North America, having an arctic or subarctic climate and a layer of permanently frozen soil several inches below the surface

understory (un′ dər stôr′ ē) the layer below the canopy in the tropical rain forest where the plants either need filtered light or are struggling to reach the canopy layer

Yanomamo (yä′ nō mä′ mō) a Native American tribe of the Amazon forest regions

INDEX

CREDITS